AN INTI
SCANNER

C000000176

Other Titles of Interest

BP255   International Radio Stations Guide

BP257   An Introduction to Amateur Radio

BP281   An Introduction to VHF/UHF for Radio Amateurs

BP293   An Introduction to Radio Wave Propagation

BP300   Setting Up An Amateur Radio Station

AN INTRODUCTION TO
SCANNERS AND SCANNING

by

I. D. POOLE
B.Sc.(Eng.), C.Eng., M.I.E.E., G3YWX

BERNARD BABANI (publishing) LTD
THE GRAMPIANS
SHEPHERDS BUSH ROAD
LONDON W6 7NF
ENGLAND

Please Note

Although every care has been taken with the production of this book to ensure that any projects, designs, modifications and/or programs etc. contained herewith, operate in a correct and safe manner and also that any components specified are normally available in Great Britain, the Publishers do not accept responsibility in any way for the failure, including fault in design, of any project, design, modification or program to work correctly or to cause damage to any other equipment that it may be connected to or used in conjunction with, or in respect of any other damage or injury that may be so caused, nor do the Publishers accept responsibility in any way for the failure to obtain specified components.

Notice is also given that if equipment that is still under warranty is modified in any way or used or connected with home-built equipment then that warranty may be void.

© 1992 BERNARD BABANI (publishing) LTD

First Published — July 1992

British Library Cataloguing in Publication Data
Poole, I. D.
    Introduction to Scanners and Scanning
    I. Title
    621.384

ISBN 0 85934 256 5

Printed and bound in Great Britain by Cox & Wyman Ltd, Reading

Contents

Page

Chapter 1
WHAT IS SCANNING? 1
  Scanner Listening 2
  The Legal Situation 3

Chapter 2
RADIO WAVES AND HOW THEY TRAVEL 5
  Polarisation 6
  Propagation 7
  The Atmosphere 7
  Ground Waves 9
  Skywaves 11
  Multiple Hops 13
  Line of Sight 13
  Tropospheric Ducting 15
  Sporadic E 15
  Summary 16

Chapter 3
TRANSMISSIONS 19
  Morse 19
  Amplitude Modulation 21
  Single Sideband 23
  Frequency Modulation 27
  Data Modes 28
  Television 31
  Facsimilie 33
  Simplex and Duplex 33

Chapter 4
SCANNERS 35
  First Things First 35
  Basic Specifications 35
  Sensitivity 36
  Selectivity 36
  Beat Frequency Oscillator 38
  Frequency Coverage 39

Chapter 4 (Continued)   **Page**

Memories 39
Steps 39
Scan and Search Rates 39
Audio Output 40
Power 40
Installation 40
Mobile Installation 41
Operation 43
Inside the Radio 44
Accessories 45

Chapter 5
AERIALS 47
Basic Principles 47
Bandwidth 47
Impedance 48
Directivity 48
Polarization 50
Feeders 52
Types of Aerial 54
Dipole 54
Yagi 57
Discone 59
Vertical 60
Rubber Ducks 62
Longwire 62
Siting 64
Installation 65

Chapter 6
THE RADIO SPECTRUM 67
Frequency Designations 67
Spectrum Allocations 69
Designations 74
Private Mobile Radio (PMR) 75
Car Phones 75
Cell Phones 75
Paging Systems 76
Marine Communications 76

Chapter 6 (Continued)   **Page**

    Callsigns 78
    Aeronautical Communications 78
    Protocol 78
    Frequencies 79
    Volmets 79
    Aeronautical Radionavigation 79
    Standard Frequency and Time Signals 81

Chapter 7
  GENERAL OPERATING PROCEDURES 83
    Operating Techniques 83
    Phonetic Alphabet 83
    Other Expressions 84
    Q Code 84
    Time 87

Chapter 8
  BROADCASTING 89
    Long and Medium Wave Bands 90
    Short Wave Broadcasting 90
    Station Identification 92
    Channels 93
    Short Wave Bands 93
    120 Metre Band 94
    90 Metre Band 94
    75 Metre Band 94
    60 Metre Band 94
    49 Metre Band 95
    41 Metre Band 95
    31 Metre Band 95
    25 Metre Band 95
    22 Metre Band 96
    19 Metre Band 96
    16 Metre Band 96
    13 Metre Band 96
    11 Metre Band 96
    VHF and UHF 97
    VHF FM (Sound) 98
    Television 99

Chapter 9	Page
AMATEUR RADIO 101	
What is Amateur Radio? 101	
Jargon 102	
Callsigns 104	
Frequency Allocations 104	
Modes 104	
Repeaters 105	
Band Plans 108	
HF Bands 108	
160 Metres 108	
80 Metres 110	
40 Metres 110	
30 Metres 110	
20 Metres 110	
17 Metres 111	
15 Metres 111	
12 Metres 111	
10 Metres 111	
VHF and UHF Bands 112	
6 Metres 113	
4 Metres 113	
2 Metres 114	
70 Centimetres 117	
Locators 119	
QSL Cards 121	
Contests 121	
Chapter 10	
CITIZEN'S BAND 125	
CB in the UK 126	
Procedure 129	
Appendix I	
GLOSSARY OF TERMINOLOGY 131	
Appendix II	
I.T.U. CALLSIGN PREFIX ALLOCATIONS 137	
Appendix III	
AMATEUR PREFIX LIST 145	

Chapter 1

WHAT IS SCANNING?

Over the past few years a new type of radio has hit the market. It is the scanner and it has given a new dimension to general coverage radio receivers. Previously the only general coverage receivers which could be bought were the short wave types. They usually only covered frequencies up to about 30 MHz and there was nothing for the listener who wanted to explore any bands which were any higher in frequency. Now this has all changed.

The first scanners which were introduced had only a limited frequency range. Usually this would be in a portion of the VHF or UHF spectrum. However, with the improvements in technology the frequency range has been considerably extended and it is now possible to buy scanners which can cover frequencies between 500 kHz (0.5 MHz) and 1.3 GHz (1,300 MHz). Technology has also meant that many new and useful facilities can be built into these sets. Then if this was not enough the size has been reduced using modern techniques so that it is possible to buy hand held scanners with a very wide frequency coverage and brimming with features and facilities.

Scanners are specifically designed for modern listening. They can be programmed to tune or scan over a number of preset frequencies and stop when they find a signal. It is this facility which gives them their name. By using this facility the receiver can be made to monitor several frequencies of interest.

For those not so interested in the VHF and UHF bands there are some sets which are aimed at the short wave bands. These sets are often called World Band Radios. They are portable and contain a number of facilities which scanners include. They usually cover frequencies up to about 30 MHz as well as the VHF FM broadcast band. This means that they are an ideal solution for those interested in short wave listening without wanting to buy a full communications receiver.

Scanner Listening

Listening to signals on the airwaves is a hobby which has captivated people since the very beginnings of radio itself. In fact there is quite a unique fascination about picking up signals from a vast variety of sources. These signals may have come from a transmitter located quite close by, or alternatively they may have come from somewhere many miles away. Part of the fascination is not knowing where the next signal may come from, or what it may be.

There are many different types of transmission which the scanner enthusiast may listen to. Probably the first and most obvious are broadcast transmissions. Using a scanner it is possible to pick up a very wide variety dependent upon the coverage of the set. Everything from the wideband FM transmissions in the VHF band to the Medium Wave services and possibly even the long range short wave transmissions as well. This in itself can be an interesting hobby. Many people enjoy listening to the wide variety of programmes from stations located within their own country. However there is a great deal to be learned by scanning across the short waves and picking up stations from all over the world.

Listening to radio amateurs is another interesting aspect of scanning. Whilst many people still associate amateur radio with Tony Hancock and his classic television comedy called the Radio Ham, there is far more to the hobby than this would indicate. There will almost certainly be several amateur bands which the scanner will be able to cover. As a result a wide variety of amateur transmissions will be able to be heard. It may be the enjoyment of eavesdropping on the conversations of radio amateurs or it may be the excitement of picking up a long distance station. All of this is part of the hobby as well as a whole lot more.

There are a number of other types of transmission which can be monitored in the UK with the appropriate licence. This can prove to be interesting as well as stimulating. One example is monitoring weather satellites. In fact it is quite possible to pick up and translate the information sent down so that an up to the minute weather map can be seen. This is just one of the many things which can be done using a scanner coupled to some of today's technology.   This is part of what makes scanning more than just another hobby.

The Legal Situation

Before proceeding any further with the subject of scanners, it is necessary to give an important warning about their use. Scanners by their very nature cover a wide range of frequencies. They can pick up signals from all sorts of users. However it may not be legal to listen to them. The actual law varies from one country to the next so it is best to check before buying a scanner or using it.

In the UK the law relating to this is contained in the Wireless Telegraphy Act. Essentially it states that the general public can only listen to properly licensed radio broadcast stations, radio amateurs and standard frequency transmissions. Any listening beyond this could be illegal. Fortunately it is possible to obtain licences to listen to some other transmissions. For example the Citizens Band (CB) transmitting licence obviously entitles one to listen to CB transmissions. Similarly the different marine licences which are issued to ships or boats, large and small, give access to these bands. In addition to this it is possible to obtain a licence to receive weather satellites (and television transmissions of course). However it is important that whatever form of listening is envisaged, the relevant aspects of the law must be borne in mind because people have been prosecuted.

Chapter 2

RADIO WAVES AND HOW THEY TRAVEL

The nature of radio waves and the way in which they travel is at the very heart of any radio communications system. These waves which are also known as electromagnetic waves are the same as light or ultra violet waves except that their wavelength and frequency are different. Fortunately it is not necessary to know much about the actual physics behind their nature. It is more than sufficient to know that they have two components: an electric field and a magnetic field which are linked together to give a wave which can travel over immense distances.

To gain more of an idea of how the wave travels it can be likened in some ways to action of the surface of a pond when a stone is dropped into the water. The ripples spread out all around, decreasing in amplitude as they travel outwards. So it is with an electromagnetic wave although its action is somewhat more complicated.

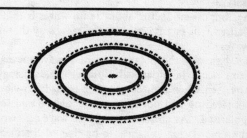

Fig. 2.1 Analogy of Ripples on a Pond Compared to Radio Waves

There are a number of points which can be noted about electromagnetic waves. The first is the wavelength. This is the distance between the same point on two successive waves. Normally the crest is chosen as a good example to visualize although any point can be chosen. This may vary in length

5

from many hundreds or thousands of metres to lengths shorter than a millimetre. It is this wavelength which is often used to give the position of a station on the Medium or Long wavebands. However, measuring the position of a station in terms of its wavelength is being used much less now. Instead its frequency is used.

The frequency can be explained using the pond analogy. It is the number of times the wave goes up and down in a given time and at a particular point in the pond. The unit generally used for frequency is the hertz and this corresponds to one cycle or wave per second. As frequencies which are encountered can be very high, the standard prefixes of kilo (kilohertz, kHz) for a thousand hertz, Mega (Megahertz, MHz) for a million hertz, and Giga (Gigahertz, GHz) for a thousand million hertz are commonly used.

Another feature which can be noted about an electromagnetic wave is its speed. Being the same as a light wave it has the same speed. Normally this is taken to be 3×10^8 metres a second or more exactly 299,792,500 metres a second in a vacuum.

Polarisation
Another important factor about radio waves is that they can be polarised. In fact it occurs in the same way that it does for light waves.

Very basically the polarisation of a wave means that the vibrations occur in a particular plane. One analogy for this could be seen when a piece of string is made to vibrate. If it only vibrated up and down then it would be said to be vertically polarised. As an electromagnetic wave has two constituents the polarisation is taken to be that of the electric field.

In fact the most common example of polarisation of an electromagnetic wave is seen with light waves. Polaroid sunglasses and lenses for cameras are seen everywhere when the sun is out. They only let light with a particular polarisation through. As light which has been reflected off a surface like water will be mainly polarised in one direction, a Polaroid material can be used to reduce the reflections. Thus if the sun was shining onto the surface of a lake, normally only the reflected light from the sun would be seen. However with a

6

Polaroid lens it would be possible to see the lake surface properly, or it might even be possible to see what is under the surface.

The same basic ideas also apply to radio waves, but because the wavelengths are so different the way in which ideas are implemented may be rather different. Even so polarisation is still very important because it has a bearing on a number of factors particularly when dealing with aerials. The main reason is that an aerial will radiate a signal having a particular polarisation. Similarly when it is receiving, an aerial will receive a signal at its maximum when the polarisation of the aerial is the same as that of the incoming signal.

Propagation

As radio waves are very similar to light waves it can be expected that they will behave in exactly the same way in many cases. One of these similarities is borne out by the fact that radio waves can be reflected and refracted. However, as the wavelength of radio waves is different to light they are reflected and refracted in cases where light is not affected or at least not to the same degree. This enables radio waves to travel over much greater distances than just the ordinary line of sight. In fact signals are regularly transmitted around the world on the short wave bands. In addition to this television and radio broadcast stations can be received beyond the horizon. However there are a number of different ways in which this can happen dependent upon the frequency in use and the different layers in the atmosphere.

The Atmosphere

The atmosphere plays an all important part in the propagation of radio waves. With its different layers extending to over 400 km above the surface of the earth there is a wide variety of different effects which can bend and reflect signals so that they can be heard over vast distances around the globe. Some layers have a significant effect on radio waves, whilst others have little or no effect.

Closest to the ground is the troposphere. It can reflect and refract radio waves to a considerable degree, generally affecting those frequencies above 30 MHz or so. As signals

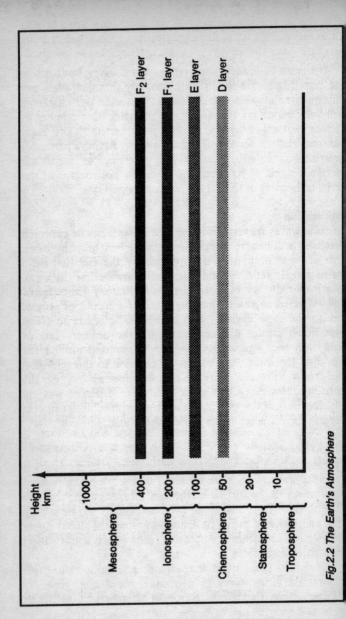

Fig.2.2 The Earth's Atmosphere

8

reflected in the troposphere do not reach any great height, distances reached when using propagation modes which occur here are generally only up to about a maximum of about 1000 km.

Most of the weather conditions which affect us occur in the troposphere, and it is no surprise to find that there are many links between the weather and the state of tropospheric propagation conditions. Because of this it is best to keep an eye on the weather chart to see if there is any likelihood of a change in conditions when it may be possible to hear stations from much further afield.

Above the troposphere there is a layer called the chemosphere. This layer has very little effect on radio wave propagation.

Further up the stratosphere and ionosphere are found. In these regions there are a number of ionised layers as shown in Figure 2.3 which can reflect or absorb radio waves. As these layers are in the upper reaches of the atmosphere it is hardly surprising to find that they are affected by conditions on the sun. In fact they will change between night and day. They will also vary according to the seasons as well as the 11 year sun spot cycle.

There are three main layers and to distinguish one from another they are given letters. The D layer is the lowest at a height of around 50 km. This only exists during the daytime when it absorbs radio waves in the lower frequencies.

Then at a height of about 110 km there is the E layer. This reflects some signals which have passed through the D layer.

Finally, at a height of between 200 and 400 km, there is the F layer. Like the E layer this one also reflects radio signals and changes significantly with time. During the night it consists of a single layer at a height of around 250 km. Then in the daytime it splits up into two layers as it receives the full measure of radiation from the sun. The lower of the two is called the F_1 and is at a height of around 200 km, whilst the upper one is called the F_2 and is at a height of between 300 and 400 km.

Ground Waves

When a signal is transmitted it spreads out in all directions

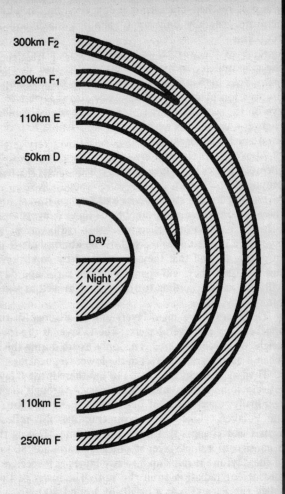

300km F₂

200km F₁

110km E

50km D

Day

Night

110km E

250km F

Fig. 2.3 Regions of the Ionosphere

from the transmitter. Some of the signal will tend to follow the curvature of the earth following the ground, and hence it is called a ground wave. This type of propagation can only be used for relatively low frequencies. This is because it is found that the losses rise with increasing frequency and this limits the use of this type of propagation to the long and medium wave bands. Above these frequencies the coverage which can be achieved is comparatively small.

Skywaves

One way in which signals can travel over very large distances is for them to reach the ionised layers in the ionosphere above the earth and be reflected back. The signals that travel in this manner are called skywaves for obvious reasons. It is this mode of propagation which is widely used on the short waves for global communication. However it is usually confined to frequencies below about 30 MHz, although at times it is possible for frequencies slightly above this to be propagated in this way.

The E and F layers bend or refract radio waves.The amount by which this occurs depends upon factors like frequency, the degree of ionisation and so forth. It is found that one frequency may be reflected by the E layer whereas a higher one may pass through it and be reflected by the F layer. A frequency which is higher still may pass through all of the layers and not be returned to earth.

In order to understand how some of the phenomena occur take the example of a transmitter located at A in Figure 2.4. Initially the frequency is set to about 1 MHz. At this frequency the ground wave is found to give reasonable coverage. However this is the main method of propagation during the day because the D layer absorbs any sky wave. As a result the signal is only heard comparatively locally.

As the signal increases in frequency it starts to penetrate the D layer. It travels on until it meets the E layer. Here it is refracted to such an extent that it is reflected back to earth and is heard at point B. In fact it is found that the signal is heard over a wide area around B. This is because the signal tends to be scattered by the uneven nature of the ionised layer and the signal will leave the transmitting aerial over a range of

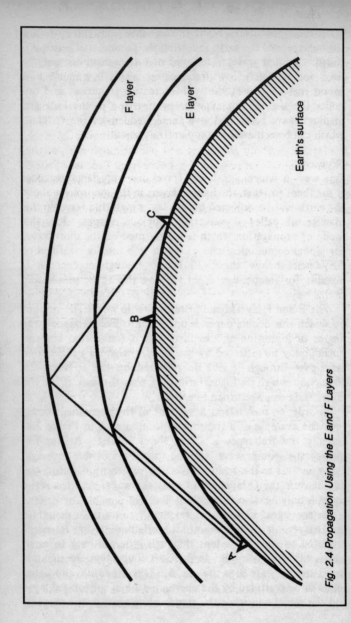

Fig. 2.4 Propagation Using the E and F Layers

F layer

E layer

Earth's surface

A

B

C

different angles. However if the signal reaches the E, or for that matter the F, layer at too high an angle it may pass straight through it. This means that there will be a zone between A and B where the signal cannot be heard. This is known as the skip zone.

If the frequency is increased still further it penetrates right through the E layer and is reflected back by one of the F layers. As this layer is higher the skip distance is much further. Eventually the signal will pass through both of the F layers and not be reflected back to earth. Because of these effects it is found that the higher frequency bands will be able to produce signals from further away. However they may not always be "open" because the degree of ionisation may fall to such an extent that the signals will pass straight through.

Multiple Hops
Very often signals will be heard over distances which are larger than would be possible with just one reflection. For example, it is quite common to hear stations from the other side of the globe whereas the maximum distance for a single reflection by the F_2 layer is about 4000 km.

Probably the most common way for signals to travel over greater distances is by multiple reflections. It is found that when a signal is reflected back to earth by the ionosphere then the earth can reflect it back up to the ionosphere as shown in Figure 2.5. In this way signals can travel to anywhere on the globe.

Line of Sight
For signals which are above those affected by the ionosphere it is the troposphere that has the major effect. However, even when conditions are normal it is still possible for signals to be heard up to distances of 100 miles or more depending upon the frequency in use. This is definitely not line of sight.

The reason for this increase in the distance is the varying density of the air. At ground level it is obviously slightly more dense than it is higher up. As the denser air has a higher refractive index this means that the refractive index of the air is higher nearer the ground. Radio waves are like light waves

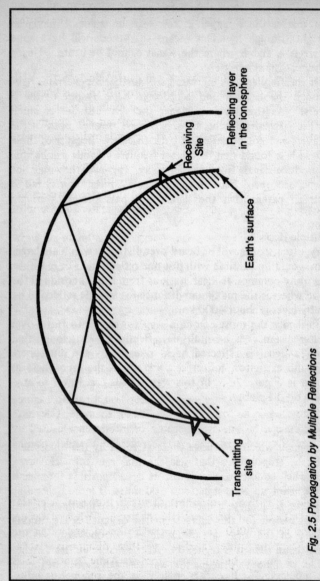

Fig. 2.5 Propagation by Multiple Reflections

and will bend towards the area of higher refractive index and this means that the signals will tend to follow the earth's curvature.

Tropospheric Ducting
One of the major effects which can cause signals in the VHF and UHF bands to be heard over greater distances is known as tropospheric ducting. It can occur as a result of what is called a temperature inversion when a layer of hot air rises above a layer of cold air. Normally the colder air is higher up because the air temperature falls with increasing height. However, when this temperature inversion occurs it is found that the hot air is less dense than the colder air and this accentuates the normal density gradient of the air. In turn this increases the change in refractive index giving a much greater refraction of radio signals.

Temperature inversions can occur in a number of ways. The most common is when there is a higher pressure area. Air heated by the warm ground rises and is replaced by cooler air. Similar conditions can also occur when a mass of warm air meets a mass of cool air in a weather front. Here the warm air rises above the cool air to give the temperature inversion.

Signals heard during a lift in conditions caused by tropospheric ducting can be heard over quite long distances. In fact it is possible for signals to travel up to 1000 km on occasions. Radio amateurs find this very useful because it means that they can make contacts over greater distance than would otherwise be possible. However it can be a source of interference to other services. For example, television reception can be impaired because of interference caused by by stations which would not be detected under normal conditions.

Sporadic E
Sporadic E is one of the most dramatic propagation effects which affects part of the VHF spectrum. When it occurs stations up to 2000 km away can be heard, and often the effect happens quite rapidly and then disappears just as quickly. As can be imagined from its name, sporadic E is not predictable. It occurs mainly in the summer months,

but unlike other modes of propagation it is not possible to determine when it will occur.

This form of propagation occurs as the result of highly ionised clouds which form in the E layer in the ionosphere. These clouds start to build up and as they form the frequencies which are reflected increase. Accordingly it is possible to find that frequencies below 30 MHz are affected first, and then frequencies higher up start to become affected. In fact it is possible for the VHF FM band to be affected and sometimes it reaches as high as the 2 metre amateur band, although this is about the maximum frequency.

The ionised clouds are relatively small. Often they are about 100 km across and only a few tens of metres thick. They are also moved around by the air currents in the upper atmosphere. This makes the effect even less predictable to use because the areas from which signals are heard change during the life of one of these clouds.

Summary

Different frequencies are affected in different ways by the various modes of propagation. Signals on low frequencies will be affected in different ways to those higher in frequency. It is not possible to give a precise picture of what happens to signals on different frequencies because conditions vary from one day to the next, but it is possible to give an overview.

It is found that transmissions below about 300 or 400 kHz will travel considerable distances using the ground wave. An example of this is the BBC Long Wave transmitter at Droitwich broadcasting on 198 kHz which can be heard over virtually all the UK and well into Western Europe.

Then as the frequency increases the ground wave becomes attenuated more. This is borne out by the fact that Medium Wave broadcast transmissions are more local in their nature. The BBC needs several transmitters to cover the UK and some of the lower power local radio stations will be heard in a radius of only up to 50 miles or so.

In spite of this it is still possible for signals to travel further. At night when the D layer in the ionosphere disappears signals from further afield can be heard and interference levels rise. Normally signals from a few hundred miles away are heard.

However some listeners who wait until the early hours when many of the transmitters are off the air have heard transatlantic stations.

A little further up in frequency the attenuation of the ground wave becomes more marked, but in compensation the D layer has less affect and signals start to be heard from further away. This becomes more noticeable around three or four Megahertz. For example, radio amateurs transmitting on frequencies around 3.5 MHz can make contacts over distances of up to 800 km by day. At night this increases so that stations over 2000 or 3000 km are heard quite easily.

As the frequency rises the effect of the ionosphere means that stations further afield are more commonplace. Around 10 MHz distances of 3000 km are quite usual by day, with major increases by night, and especially around dawn and dusk. At these times stations from the other side of the world can be heard quite often.

Between frequencies of about 15 and 30 MHz the effect of the ionosphere appears to be slightly different. Often the most distant stations are audible during the day. In fact most of the stations could be more than 3000 km away and quite possibly at the other side of the globe. Then at night the number of stations which can be heard is often much reduced. However this is very dependent upon the season and the number of sunspots.

Above 30 MHz the effect of the ionosphere becomes much less. Only during periods of high sunspot activity are these frequencies affected and then the maximum is just above 50 MHz. However other effects become more noticeable. Tropospheric ducting becomes increasingly important, and so does sporadic E which can bring stations in from distances up to 2000 km. However the limit of sporadic E is about 150 MHz, although it does affect the VHF FM broadcast band quite often during the summer months.

For frequencies above 150 MHz the main means by which long distance signals are heard is tropospheric ducting. Apart from this stations will be heard over distances of up to 150 km or so, but this is very dependent upon the power of the transmitter and the aerials in use.

Chapter 3

TRANSMISSIONS

Tuning around all the frequencies which can be picked up on a scanner it is possible to hear all manner of peculiar noises. Some of them will be intelligible but a lot of them will not be. It may be possible to detect some morse signals, some other signals which appear to be keyed or switched in some way, noises which sound as though they may have been speech at one time but are certainly not intelligible now, and a whole host of other signals. In fact very few of these signals could be made to yield any intelligible sound if they were picked up on a normal domestic radio set.

The reason for all these different types of transmission is that they are all communicating in different ways. Each type of transmission has its own characteristics and advantages. Some signals like morse can be copied fairly easily if the code is known. Other signals are different forms of data transmission some of which are quite comprehensive in the way they work. They can use a computer linked up to the transmitter and receiver so that the data can be coded in the right way before it is transmitted or decoded when it is received. Other signals sound like garbled speech and are an efficient form of voice communication. The signal has been generated in such a way that it makes the best use of the available power and frequency space. Because of this, some special electronic circuitry is needed in the receiver if it is to be copied.

For the scanner user to be able to get the best out of the set it is useful to know a little about each mode or type of transmission. This may enable the listener to use the set to its best advantage, particularly under poor conditions.

Morse

Morse is the simplest and the oldest way of transmitting information over the radio. It simply involves turning a radio transmission on and off as shown in Figure 3.1. This can be done using a simple morse key which the operator presses down when he wants to make a sound in the receiver. A short

19

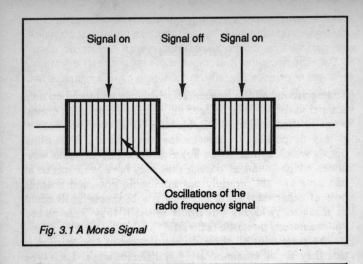

Fig. 3.1 A Morse Signal

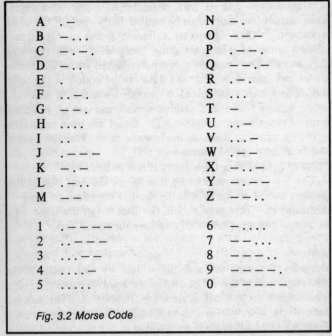

A	.−		N	−.
B	−...		O	−−−
C	−.−.		P	.−−.
D	−..		Q	−−.−
E	.		R	.−.
F	..−.		S	...
G	−−.		T	−
H	....		U	..−
I	..		V	...−
J	.−−−		W	.−−
K	−.−		X	−..−
L	.−..		Y	−.−−
M	−−		Z	−−..
1	.−−−−		6	−....
2	..−−−		7	−−...
3	...−−		8	−−−..
4	....−		9	−−−−.
5	.....		0	−−−−−

Fig. 3.2 Morse Code

sound is called a dot whilst a longer one is called a dash. The dots and dashes can then be used to make up letters, numbers and punctuation marks in accordance with the morse code.

Surprisingly morse is still one of the most effective ways of modulating or encoding information onto a radio signal. Even now after all the tremendous technological advances which have been made since radio was first used around 1900 it is still used quite extensively. This is because it possesses several distinct advantages.

One advantage is that a morse signal can be heard and copied when it may not be possible to copy another type of signal. The reason for this lies in its simplicity; it is only a radio carrier being turned on and off. As the operator only has to detect whether the signal is present or not, morse can be copied when the levels are very low. A complicated signal carrying sound is much more difficult to read.

The other advantage that morse possesses is that it only takes up a small bandwidth because of its relatively slow signalling rate. This means that narrow filters can be used to cut out a lot of interference.

However, one disadvantage of morse transmissions is that not all receivers and scanners can resolve them properly so that the characteristic audio tone is produced. For this to be produced a piece of circuitry called a beat frequency oscillator is needed. This is described in Chapter 4.

Amplitude Modulation
Even though morse has many advantages it still cannot replace the spoken word, and it cannot be used to transmit entertainment. In order to be able to transmit speech and music the radio signal must be modulated or changed in some way by the sounds. There are several ways of doing this, but the most obvious is to modulate the amplitude or strength of the signal.

Amplitude modulation or AM is the method which is used by broadcast stations on the long, medium and short wave bands. Its main advantage is its simplicity. This is particularly true in the receiver where the circuitry needed if a radio is to receive it is very simple. This means that radios for these wavebands can be made quite cheaply.

21

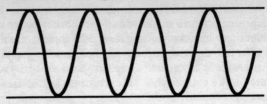

a) A radio frequency carrier

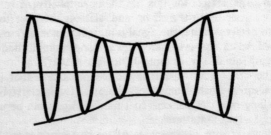

b) The carrier with some amplitude modulation

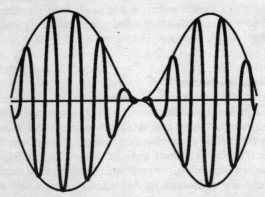

c) 100% modulation

Fig. 3.3 Amplitude Modulation of a Radio Frequency Signal

Unfortunately AM has some drawbacks. It is very inefficient in its use of transmitter power and bandwidth. As a result it is not used for communications purposes. In order to understand the reason for this it is necessary to look into a bit of background theory. Figure 3.3(a) shows an unmodulated carrier. When modulation is applied, it will vary as shown in Figure 3.3(b). However it can be seen that there is still some room to add some more modulation to it. In fact the maximum amount of modulation which can be put onto a radio signal occurs when the envelope falls to zero and rises to twice the original level as shown in Figure 3.3(c). When this level is reached then the carrier is said to have 100% modulation.

Even when the carrier is fully modulated it is found that the power utilisation is still poor. To investigate this further it is necessary to look at what happens to the frequency spectrum at the various stages. To simplify matters take the example of the modulating signal being a 1 kHz tone. The same arguments are true for speech or music but a single tone makes the diagram less complicated.

Figure 3.4(a) shows an unmodulated radio frequency signal. When it is modulated by the 1 kHz tone it is found that two new signals appear which are called sidebands for obvious reasons. One is 1 kHz below the main signal and the other is 1 kHz above it. The unfortunate fact is that the sidebands are the part of the signal that actually carry the sound and they are only a quarter of the power of the carrier. In fact the only purpose of the carrier is to act as a reference during the demodulation stage. From this point of view AM is very inefficient in terms of power.

In addition to this AM is inefficient in its use of frequency space or bandwidth. Looking at Figure 3.5 the spectrum of a typical speech or music signal is shown. From this it can be seen that the actual amount of bandwidth or frequency space is twice that of the original audio signal. This is why AM is not used much outside the broadcasting service.

Single Sideband
Single sideband, or SSB, is widely used for long distance speech communications. Radio amateurs make great use of it as do many professional and commercial users like ship-to-

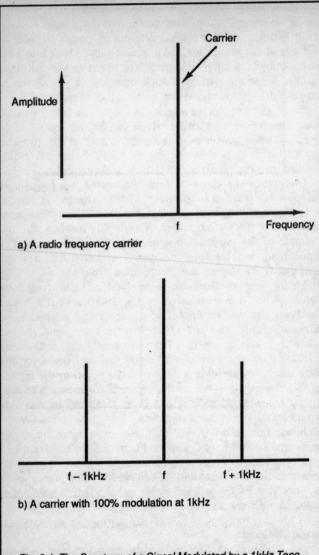

a) A radio frequency carrier

b) A carrier with 100% modulation at 1kHz

Fig. 3.4 The Spectrum of a Signal Modulated by a 1kHz Tone

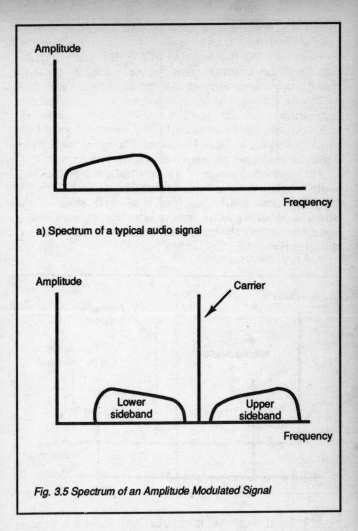

a) Spectrum of a typical audio signal

Fig. 3.5 Spectrum of an Amplitude Modulated Signal

shore services, long distance communications to aircraft, and so forth.

When received on an ordinary radio it sounds very garbled and totally incomprehensible. This hides its advantages which make it the most efficient form of voice communication, particularly under poor conditions when the signal is weak and the interference is high.

Essentially SSB is a derivative of AM. It is basically an AM signal with the unwanted parts removed to leave only those that contribute to carrying the speech sounds themselves.

One of the disadvantages of AM was that it possessed a large carrier which only acted as a reference during demodulation. As this can be provided by the receiver there is little point in keeping it. When the carrier is removed this leaves a signal containing just two sidebands and no carrier.

The other disadvantage of AM was that it occupied a bandwidth which was twice that of the radio. As both sidebands carry the same information (one is a mirror image of the other) it seems logical to remove one. Having done this, a signal containing only one sideband and no carrier remains as shown in Figure 3.6. This is SSB.

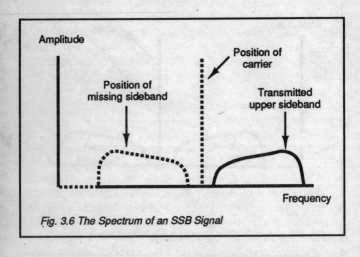

Fig. 3.6 The Spectrum of an SSB Signal

As both sidebands are identical except that one is a mirror image of the other, it is possible to use either one. However it makes matters easier if a convention is adopted to govern which one is used. Normally the lower sideband is used on frequencies below 10 MHz whilst the upper sideband is used on frequencies above 10 MHz.

In order to resolve a single sideband signal it is necessary to be able to reinsert the carrier within the receiver. This is done using an oscillator called a beat frequency oscillator (BFO) or a carrier insertion oscillator (CIO). Both are the same despite the two names. Once the carrier has been reinserted in the demodulation process the original audio is obtained.

The main problem with SSB is that it is necessary to reinsert the carrier at exactly the right frequency. Often it is possible to tolerate an offset of about 100 Hz and this will tend to raise or lower the pitch of the audio, giving it a rather distinctive sound. However, if the offset is too large it will become rather difficult to copy the signal.

Frequency Modulation

Modulating the amplitude of a radio frequency signal is the most obvious way of applying audio to it. Even so it is not the only way as there are a number of other methods each with their own advantages. One is frequency modulation which finds many uses in a wide selection of applications.

As the name implies frequency modulation or FM entails changing the frequency of a signal according to the intensity of the modulation. Looking at Figure 3.7 it can be seen that the frequency of the signal increases as the voltage of the modulating signal increases, and conversely the frequency falls as the voltage decreases.

The amount by which the frequency changes is called the deviation. This can be fairly small (around 3 kHz) for narrow band frequency modulation (NBFM) or much wider (possibly about 75 kHz) in the case of wide band FM.

FM normally finds most of its uses in the higher frequencies above 30 MHz or so. One is the lowest frequency users is Citizen's Band operating around 27 MHz. FM is also used for many commercial mobile applications. However it is probably most widely known for the VHF FM broadcast service which operates in the band 87.5 to 108 MHz.

The main advantage of FM is its immunity to noise. As all the information is carried in the variations of frequency, the receiver can be made almost immune to any amplitude variations. It is found that a lot of the received noise will be amplitude noise, so once a signal has reached a certain level,

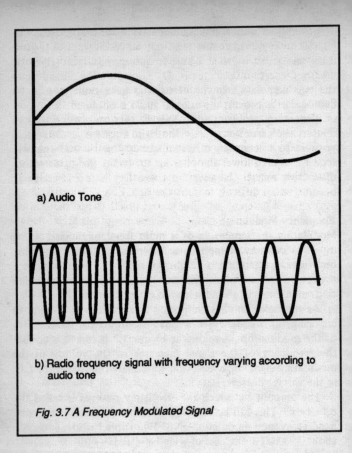

a) Audio Tone

b) Radio frequency signal with frequency varying according to
   audio tone

Fig. 3.7 A Frequency Modulated Signal

then the background noise will be fairly low. Another advantage is that the effects of fading can be made to be unnoticeable. This is particularly important for mobile applications where signal levels can fluctuate quite rapidly when the vehicle is moving.

Data Modes

Apart from morse and speech or music it is also possible to send data over the air. With the increase in the use of computers and other requirements for sending data, this area

28

of communications is undergoing a rapid time of growth. In fact technology has gone a long way since the days of the old teleprinters like those seen on the Saturday television reporting the sports results.

Generally data communications use various forms of Frequency Shift Keying or FSK. In its basic form this mode switches the frequency of a signal between two different frequencies. The system is operated in this way because it is much easier for electronic systems to distinguish between two defined states rather than having to detect the presence or absence of a signal such as a morse signal.

There are two ways of transmitting FSK. The first is to shift the frequency of the carrier itself. This method is commonly used on frequencies below about 30 MHz. However on higher frequencies it is more usual to modulate the carrier with an audio tone. The frequency of this tone is then switched between the two frequencies.

Usually the data from computers or teleprinters is generated in terms of two voltage levels (often termed "1" and "0" or "high" and "low"). To convert these into the required tones for transmission a unit called a modem is used. This performs the same basic task as a modem used for transmitting data between computers along telephone lines. In addition to this some forms of data communication involve complicated message handling between the two ends. If these modes are used then often another unit may be needed. Alternatively a computer could perform the task.

Data transmissions can take a variety of forms. The first which was used over radio incorporated teleprinters. These used a code called the Murray Code. Today many computers talk to one another over the air and they will often use other codes specially devised for the purpose or even ASCII (American Standard Code for Information Interchange) which is the normal code used for computer communications.

One form of data communication which is becoming very popular within amateur radio circles is called packet radio. With this mode small packets of data are sent out to the receiver. After each packet has been successfully received an acknowledgement is sent back and the next one is sent. If the data is not received correctly then the packet will be

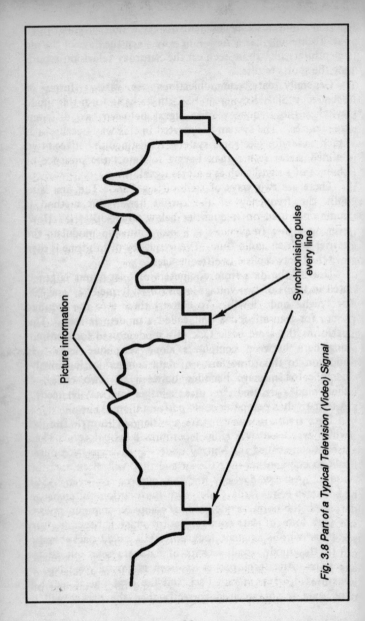

Fig. 3.8 Part of a Typical Television (Video) Signal

Picture information

Synchronising pulse
every line

repeated until it is received correctly. By adopting this approach virtually error free copy can be achieved.

Television

The make up of a television signal is quite complicated, and a full description of its parameters is beyond the scope of this book. Even so a brief and simplified explanation is worthwhile.

A television signal consists of two components. The first is the sound or audio signal, and the second is the vision or picture signal. Whilst the sound signal is quite straightforward the same is not quite true for the vision. Very basically the picture is split up into a number of horizontal lines: 625 in the case of broadcast television in the UK. Each line is scanned in turn and the light intensity at a given point is converted into a voltage. This means that an irregular waveform is generated according to the light variation across the line.

For information to be displayed in a meaningful fashion the transmitter and receiver must be linked together so that the same point is being scanned at the same time. To achieve this a synchronisation pulse is added by the transmitter at the end of each line to give an overall video waveform like that shown in Figure 3.8. Other synchronisation pulses are added to ensure that each complete picture is synchronised as well.

Having obtained the video and audio signals the next stage is to modulate them onto the radio frequency carrier. In general the video signal is amplitude modulated, but one sideband is partially removed to conserve bandwidth. The sound signal is then frequency modulated onto a carrier on a different frequency. This is done so that the two signals do not interfere with one another.

This form of television is known as fast scan television because the pictures are repeated faster than the eye can detect. As a result of its speed it needs to take up a lot of spectrum space. In some instances it might be necessary to send pictures over a link with a much lower bandwidth. This can be done if the speed at which the signals is sent is reduced and possibly the definition is reduced. This form of television is naturally called slow scan television and finds a number of uses, often in more specialised applications.

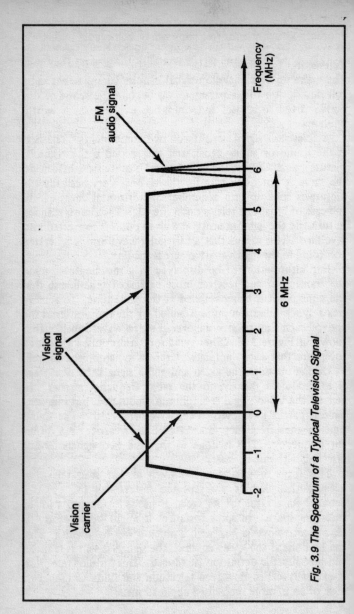

Fig. 3.9 The Spectrum of a Typical Television Signal

Facsimile

The use of facsimile or fax machines is greatly on the increase today, and not only on the telephone lines. Many fax signals are transmitted over the air. Essentially the system they use is very much akin to a slow scan television system.

Simplex and Duplex

There are a number of different ways in which transmitter receiver systems can work. In some systems the transmitter is turned on only when a message needs to be sent, whereas in others the transmitters at either end are left on all the time. The names simplex and duplex indicate how the system works.

In a simplex system the transmitter and receiver are both tuned to the same frequency. The receiver would normally be left on and the transmitter would only transmit when a message needs to be sent. CB transceivers and the like use a simplex mode of operation. It is simple, effective and meets the needs of many users.

However a simplex system is not always adequate. When using simplex it is necessary to co-ordinate which transmitter is to be transmitting at any one time. Often the person who is transmitting will have to make this clear by saying "over" or using some similar terminology. If this is not done then communications can become quite chaotic, and this can happen quite easily.

To overcome this problem a duplex system can be used. This involves the two transmitters using different frequencies and transmitting all of the time. The receivers will be set to the frequency of the other transmitter (which is different to its companion transmitter) and therefore it will be able to receive all the time. In this way it is possible to hold normal conversations. Cellphones and many other systems use duplex.

In addition to simplex and duplex there is a further system which is known as half duplex. In essence it is half way between simplex and duplex. The base station is able to transmit and receive at the same time. Then the mobile or remote stations which will only be able to transmit or receive and not both together. Like a full duplex system a half duplex one needs to use two frequencies, one for the base station to transmit and another for it to receive. The advantage

33

of it is that the base station which will normally be the controller can listen all the time. The remote stations which do not need the capability to listen all the time will be able to use simpler and less expensive equipment.

Chapter 4

SCANNERS

It is quite possible to own and use a scanner without any knowledge of what goes on inside. However if the right scanner is to be chosen then a basic knowledge of some of the technical terms and what they mean is very useful. This also helps when operating it because the best use can be made of all the facilities.

First Things First

Today's radios, whether they are scanners or world band radios, use some of the latest technology. They will almost certainly employ a microprocessor to give them all the facilities which are required. Whilst they are designed to be easy to operate they will have a very wide variety of facilities. Some of these facilities are self explanatory and easy to use. Others may require a little more knowledge about the radio. This can be true even if scanners have been used before as there are always differences between one scanner and the next. Accordingly it is always best to read the instruction manual before using the radio. If this is not done then some useful facilities can be missed.

In addition to this the manual will detail any precautions which must be taken with the radio. It is all too easy to adopt the attitude "if all else fails read the instructions". However in some cases this can be disastrous, especially when dealing with power supplies and batteries. Simply putting the batteries in the wrong way round may damage the receiver.

Basic Specifications

When looking at the glossy advertising sheets for different scanners there will be a number of specifications which are mentioned. Sometimes they can be confusing, but with a little explanation they need not be too hard to understand.

Scanners come in two basic varieties. The first type is intended for base station or desk top use. The scanners which fall into this category are generally a little larger and will have

35

a large number of facilities. For those people who like to take their scanners with them handheld units are available. Generally they have a slightly reduced specification and possibly a few less facilities, but in spite of this they still perform very well.

Sensitivity
One of the first considerations of any receiver or scanner is its sensitivity. This is the ability to pick up weak signals. Not only does it depend on the amount by which the receiver can amplify the signal, but also the amount of noise which is generated by the internal circuits.

In general there is no problem with achieving sufficient amplification. However, to achieve a good noise performance can be a little more difficult and it is chiefly governed by the noise performance of the first stages of the receiver. The receiver's noise performance is particularly important for frequencies in the VHF portion of the spectrum and above. Below this atmospheric noise is comparatively high and masks any receiver noise.

The sensitivity of a scanner or receiver will generally be expressed in terms of a certain number of microvolts at the aerial input to give a particular signal-to-noise ratio. For a typical scanner a sensitivity of less than one microvolt for a 10 dB signal-to-noise ratio on SSB or CW would be quite acceptable. On AM the figures are likely to be slightly worse at around one or two microvolts for a 10 dB signal-to-noise ratio.

When specifying the sensitivity for FM signals SINAD figures are generally used. A figure of less than one microvolt to give a 12 dB SINAD is quite typical.

Selectivity
The selectivity of a receiver is another important feature which will be mentioned in the data. Essentially it is the ability to accept signals only on the wanted frequency or channel and to reject those which are on another one. It is particularly important because a receiver with poor selectivity will pick up stations on unwanted channels causing interference to the wanted ones as shown in Figure 4.1.

36

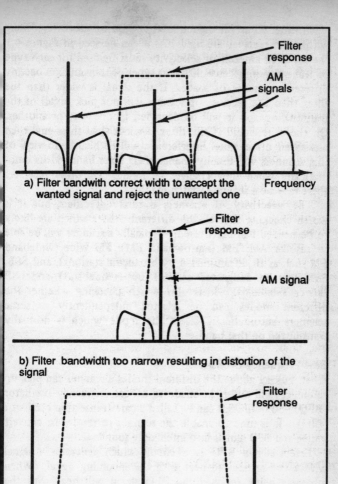

a) Filter bandwith correct width to accept the
wanted signal and reject the unwanted one

b) Filter bandwidth too narrow resulting in distortion of the
signal

c) Filter bandwidth too wide allowing interference to be picked
up from neighbouring signals

Fig. 4.1 Receiver Selectivity

In order to attain the required amount of selectivity, filters within the receiver are used. As it can be seen in Figure 4.1 the required amount of selectivity must be used for each type of transmission because different types of transmission occupy different amounts of space. If the signal is wider than the filter then the receiver or scanner will not pick up all of the transmission and it will be degraded in one way or another. On the other hand if the filter is wider than the signal then unwanted off channel interference will be heard. In view of this scanners will usually change their filter bandwidths automatically when they change the mode. On other receivers there may be a separate switch for this.

The selectivity of scanners is rarely specified, but it is worth checking that all the different modes which are likely to be needed can be covered. Typically a scanner will be able to resolve AM, FM (narrowband FM), FM Wide (wideband FM such as that transmitted by broadcast stations), and SSB. SSB may be designated as USB (upper sideband), and LSB (lower sideband). It is also worth checking whether the different modes can be selected independently as some scanners automatically select the mode which is normally transmitted on that band.

Beat Frequency Oscillator
When talking about the different modes a scanner can pick up reference will often be made to a beat frequency oscillator (BFO). Sometimes it can be called a carrier insertion oscillator (CIO). It is used to enable the scanner to resolve or convert morse and SSB signals into intelligible sounds.

Essentially a BFO is a circuit which generates a signal within the scanner to beat with the incoming signal. When morse is being received the BFO signal will beat with the morse to give an audible tone. For SSB it performs the same function but instead of producing a steady audio note it recovers the speech or whatever is being transmitted. To get the best results the BFO must be placed at the same position relative to the signal where the original carrier would have been. If the BFO is offset from this frequency then the pitch of the recovered audio will be either higher or lower than it should be.

Frequency Coverage

It is always wise to have a good look at the frequency coverage of the scanner. Not only is it worth making sure that the highest and lowest frequencies extend to the correct limits, but it is also worth checking all the frequencies in between. Often scanners will cover a number of different bands which have gaps between them. It is quite possible that these gaps may just occur where transmissions of particular interest are located.

Memories

One of the features of scanners is that it is possible to store different frequencies of interest. Having stored them, it is then an easy matter to monitor them using the scan features or to manually call them up. By doing this much time-consuming searching for stations or re-entering of frequencies can be eliminated.

Most scanners today will have a very large number of memory channels. Even many handhelds will have upwards of 200, and many base station ones will have more.

Steps

On most scanners it is possible to change the step size. This is important because the spacing between stations changes from one band to another. Typically it might be possible to have steps of 5, 10, 12.5, 25 and 100 kHz steps. Smaller steps will often be needed if operation below 30 MHz is required because stations are not always conveniently spaced. The major exception is AM broadcast stations on the short wave broadcast bands which are spaced every 5 kHz.

Scan and Search Rates

These figures refer to the rate at which the scanner can change its frequency. When scanning the receiver has to move to each frequency in turn and check whether there is a station there. This all takes a finite amount of time. Also when scanning memories which may be spaced well apart from one another the time taken is longer than searching channels which are next to one another. Normally scan rates of between 10 and

20 channels a second are attainable, and search rates a little better than this are usually quoted.

Audio Output
The audio output is the level of the audio signal which is presented to the loudspeaker from the electronic circuitry. Most desk top scanners tend to be rated at around about a watt, and this is quite adequate for listening in most environments. Handheld scanners are not quite so powerful as they are designed to run from batteries and they have to be a little more economical with their use of power. A typical handheld will have an output of about 100 mW (one tenth of a watt). This is about the same level one would expect from a small transistor radio, and it should be enough for most purposes.

Power
The power requirements for the scanner are usually mentioned in the specifications as different scanners will use different amounts of power and they will use different sources. Desk top models will generally be able to use mains, although some are designed specifically for running from 12 volt supplies making them suitable for running from a car. However it should be noted that they consume a reasonable amount of current, often about 1 amp.

Handheld scanners invariably use internal batteries, although some may have the capability of using an alternative external supply. For these handhelds the current consumption is quite important. If the consumption is high then the batteries will need replacing more frequently.

Installation
In most cases installation of a desk top scanner will simply consist of fitting a mains plug to the power lead and attaching the aerial. However if the best is to be made of the unit then it is worth spending a little time considering where it can be located. Ideally it should be on a desk top so that band plans and reference books can be used quite easily, or a log book can be filled in if one is used.

The scanner should also be located in a place without too high a level of background noise otherwise listening can be very much more difficult. Conversely it is also a good idea to put the set in a place where it will not cause too much annoyance to others.

It is also wise to keep the scanner in a place where it will not be subject to extremes of temperature. In particular it should be kept out of direct sunlight if possible. Moisture is another consideration and the unit should be kept in a reasonably dry atmosphere.

The set should also be placed away from sources of interference, especially if the internal aerial has to be used. Televisions, computers and their monitors are great generators of noise and mush, particularly around the lower frequencies. Fluorescent lights are also renowned for their interference which can be detected well above the top frequency limits of any scanners on the market today. Then there are the more intermittent noises like the clicks which are picked up from fridges and freezers as the compressor motors start and stop.

Finally there should be reasonable access for aerial leads. If anything but casual listening is envisaged then the aerial on the set will not be adequate. To obtain the best results the aerial will have to be located away from the set and this will usually mean having a coaxial or TV down lead type of cable and this will have to be suitably routed through the house.

Mobile Installation

Many scanners are designed to be operated from a car and this form of operation is becoming increasingly popular. When installing a scanner into a car it is very much like installing a normal car radio but there are a few differences and these should be borne in mind.

As the radio is unlikely to fit into the standard car radio slot a suitable site has to be located. It should be easy to operate and if the scanner's internal speaker is to be used this should not be masked to allow the sound out. To help the fitting of the set there are a number of special mounting brackets which are available. Some of them allow the set to be removed quickly so that it can be placed out of sight when the car is unattended. This is very useful in view of the ever increasing rate of thefts from cars.

Interference can be a problem with mobile scanners. Like ordinary car radios they pick up interference, but in view of the fact that they are designed to be very sensitive they can pick up interference more easily as well. As a standard precaution the earth connection from the set should be taken via a short thick lead directly to the car metalwork. But before doing this check that the metalwork on the set is not at 12 volts. Cars these days have a negative earth and sets take this into consideration but occasionally some much older cars are wired up with a positive earth.

If the scanner is well earthed and interference still persists then a little detective work is required. There are two ways in which interference can enter a scanner. One is from the aerial through the aerial socket. The other is through the power leads.

The first step is to determine which way the interference is getting in. The simplest way is to remove the aerial lead. If the noise disappears then the interference is coming in through the aerial. If it does not then it is coming along the power leads.

If the power leads are carrying the interference then it is possible to fit an in-line suppressor which can be obtained from most motor parts factors. Whilst this will improve matters it may not remove the problem completely, and it is often best to remove the interference at source any way.

Many of the sources of noise are quite obvious. Windscreen wipers, direction indicators and the like are prime examples and they can often be cured by placing a suppressor capacitor across them. In the case of windscreen wipers the metal cases are not always well earthed so a braid from the case to the chassis often helps. Noises that appear like a rasping whine that go up and down with the speed of the engine usually come from the alternator. Again a suppressor can cure this. Direct ignition noise can be helped by placing a suppressor from the battery side of the coil to ground.

If the interference is being picked up by the aerial it means that the noise is being transmitted and the car metalwork is not acting as a screen very well. One alternative is to move the aerial away from the engine and the source of interference.

Another common problem is that the bonnet may not have a good electrical connection to the rest of the car. Many new cars these days have a braid across one of the bonnet hinges to prevent this, so it is worth checking and possibly fixing one in if necessary.

Operation

There is a very wide variety of scanners on the market these days ranging from the cheapest handheld sets right up to the top of the range desk top models. Despite this variety the basic mode of operation of all scanners is basically the same. As a result of this there are a number of keys and controls which are the same on all scanners.

Probably the most obvious control which all scanners have is a keypad. This makes them stand out from other types of receiver which by and large do not have keypads.

The keypads have a variety of keys to give them the flexibility which is commonplace with today's sets. Obviously the numeric keys are used for entering frequency information or selecting the number of a channel. In addition to this there are a number of other keys used to control other functions in the set.

One of these functions is the Delay. It is used to govern the amount of time the scanner will stay on a frequency after a signal has disappeared. This facility can be used when a station makes a number of short transmissions in quick succession before staying off the air for a longer time. By using the delay the scanner can be made to catch all the transmissions and then move on once they have finished.

The Enter and Memory keys are virtually self explanatory. They are used for entering different frequencies into the memory and then recalling them later as required.

The Lock-out facility is used to prevent particular channels from being scanned. It may be that one channel in a scan is occupied with a transmission that is not of any interest. Alternatively it may have a high level of interference. Under either of these circumstances the channel, or a number of channels, can be locked out to prevent the scanner from monitoring them.

A mode switch is included on many scanners to select AM, Narrow Band or Wide Band FM, SSB, etc. If one is not present then the set will select the mode normally used on that band. Usually this is perfectly satisfactory, but it does not give the advanced listener the flexibility which might be needed on some occasions.

Most scanners will possess a squelch control. This is used to mute or switch off the audio when no signals are present. This is particularly useful for FM because high levels of background noise are present when no signal is present. The squelch control should be adjusted so that it just does not allow the audio to come on when there is no station on channel. By adjusting it like this even the weakest signals can be heard.

It is obviously not possible to give a complete description of all the controls on a scanner because they will vary from one set to the next. To know how to use a particular scanner the best advice is to read the instruction manual carefully even though it may not be written in the most clear and concise English. By doing this all the features of the set should be revealed and it will be possible to use it to the full.

Inside the Radio

Once the scanner has been in use for a while there may be a temptation to look inside it. Beware! It is very easy to damage the inside of the radio and the warranty will be invalidated. Most scanners have a very wide variety of facilities and to achieve this they are packed full of electronics. Without knowing how to take it apart it is very easy to damage things. In fact merely touching some components can destroy them because the static electricity on the body can blow some components inside them. Also if any adjustable components are moved then this can degrade the performance of the set and without the proper test equipment it may not be possible to return it to its original state.

Finally, if the set is mains powered then there is the possibility of an electric shock. It is a golden rule that no piece of electronic equipment should be opened when it is connected to the mains.

Accessories

There is a wide variety of accessories which can be bought for scanners now. Some consist of very sophisticated units which can extend the capabilities of the set quite considerably and open new fields of interest which might have never been considered before. Others can be quite simple, but can still add to the enjoyment of operating the set.

Headphones: One of the simplest accessories must be a pair of headphones and they are also quite cheap. In fact almost any pair of headphones will be quite satisfactory and there is no need to spend too much on them. The relatively cheap ones for use with portable stereos and the like are ideal and enable the set to be used without annoying everybody round about.

Extension Speakers: Sometimes it may be necessary to put an extension speaker onto the scanner. As the speaker in the scanner will not be very large, an external one may give an improvement in quality. Most speakers these days are 8 Ω and it is usual for the scanner to require speakers to be about this. Before buying it is worth just checking that everything matches.

When installing the speaker make sure that the speaker lead cannot short out. Usually there is no problem, but if the lead is worn or screw terminals are used there is a possibility that a whisker of copper wire may cause a short. If this happens it is almost certain to damage the set so it is worth checking.

Interfaces: To extend the capabilities of the scanner there are a number of different interfaces which can be bought. Morse decoders and interfaces for packet radio and Amtor are quite common. It is also possible to receive slow scan television.

Sometimes specialized units can be obtained which will later connect to a computer. However a growing trend with IBM PC compatible computers is to have a card which will plug into the computer. Only the software is then needed to run a variety of different applications.

Apart from receiving the more usual terrestrial communications, there is a growing interest in receiving weather satellite pictures. This can be accomplished fairly easily with the right interface and software. The main requirement is that the scanner should have a wideband FM position which can be utilized on the satellite frequencies. This is required because the satellites' transmissions are in excess of the bandwidth offered for the Narrow Band modes.

Chapter 5

AERIALS

A good aerial is very important if a scanner or any radio receiver is to operate properly. If a poor aerial is used then there is no hope of the set reaching its full potential, whereas a good aerial will enable much weaker signals to be picked up with ease. There is no point in spending several hundreds of pounds on a good scanner and then forgetting about the aerial.

To many people the subject of aerials can seem a complete mystery. Fortunately there is no need to have a deep knowledge about them because there is a good variety of aerials designed specifically for scanner use available in the shops. Even so it is worth knowing a little so that they can be installed to give the best performance.

Basic Principles

The purpose of the aerial is to pick up the radio waves and convert them into electrical currents which can be passed into the set. Here they can be processed and converted into audio signals which can be heard.

The theory behind the operation of aerials can become quite complicated, and fortunately it is not necessary to go into this in any detail at all. However a basic knowledge of a number of aspects of aerials is quite important. It gives a better understanding of how to ensure that they can be made to operate at their best. Topics like bandwidth, directivity, and polarization are all important and do not need any great technical understanding.

Bandwidth

An aerial acts very much like a tuned circuit. This means that it will only operate efficiently over a band of frequencies. Outside this range it will pick up some signals but it will be very inefficient.

The actual frequency at which the aerial is resonant is chiefly governed by the length of its elements. In fact it is possible to calculate how long the elements should be for a particular frequency of operation. As a rule the longer the element the lower the frequency of operation.

The majority of aerials have a comparatively narrow bandwidth. In many instances this is quite acceptable. For example an aerial to be used on the 2 metre amateur band would only need to operate over the range 144 to 146 MHz. This range is quite small and can be accommodated by most aerial designs. For receiving the VHF FM broadcasts it would need to operate over the range 87.5 to 108 MHz. This is a much wider bandwidth and the aerial design has to be a little more exacting otherwise the performance will fall significantly at either end of the range.

To cover a range which is any larger than this then special wideband aerials are needed. These designs tend not to be quite as efficient as similar sized narrowband aerials but they do give a satisfactory performance over a much wider band.

Impedance

To a radio frequency signal an aerial appears to have a certain impedance. Whilst it is not necessary to go into all the technical ins and outs, it does have an impact on the choice of parts for the aerial system. If the aerial system is to work efficiently the impedance of the aerial, the feeder or coax and the input to the scanner must all be the same. By doing this the maximum amount of signal is transferred from the aerial to the feeder and then into the receiver. For example, scanners have a 50 Ω impedance.

Directivity

When talking about the directivity of an aerial it is easier to think of it as a transmitting aerial and how the power it radiates is distributed. Then the same conclusions hold true for it as a receiving aerial.

The radiation from a practical aerial is not the same in all directions. In fact the intensity of the radiation will vary around the aerial from place to place and a plot of the pattern of this radiation is called a polar diagram. Essentially this plots a curve around an aerial showing the intensity of the radiation at each point. An example for an aerial known as a dipole is shown in Figure 5.1.

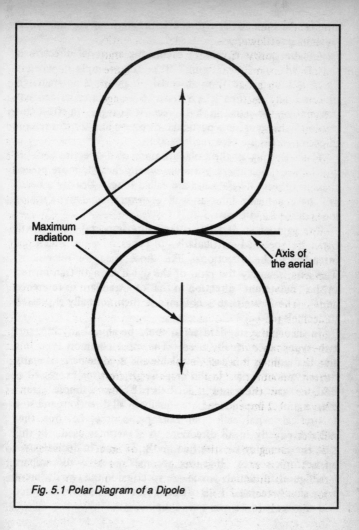

Maximum
radiation

Axis of
the aerial

Fig. 5.1 Polar Diagram of a Dipole

The radiation pattern of an aerial is very important. By adding further sections to an aerial it is possible to make it very directive responding to stations better in one direction than another. Directive aerials may need to be used because stations only in a given area or direction need to be heard and others have to be reduced in strength to cut down the levels of interference.

Another major advantage of making an aerial directive is that it will have some gain. Take the example of when a signal is transmitted from an aerial. If power is not radiated in one direction then it will have to be radiated in another one making the signal in that direction stronger. In effect this "beams" the signal in a particular direction and for this reason directive aerials are often called beams.

When looking at the polar diagram of a directive aerial it will be seen that there are areas where there is more power than in others. These areas are called lobes. Usually a beam will have a major lobe as well as several smaller or minor lobes as shown in Figure 5.2.

The gain of an aerial is often quite important and it will often be specified particularly on types of aerial which are intended to be directional like those used for televisions. This gain is simply the ratio of the signal strength transmitted in the "maximum" direction to that of a standard or reference aerial. The figure that is obtained is then normally expressed in decibels (dB).

In theory the standard aerial could be almost anything but two types are normally used. The most common type is a simple dipole as it is easily available and it is the basis of many other types of aerial. In this case the gain is often expressed as dBd, i.e. gain expressed in decibels (dB) over a dipole. However, a dipole does not radiate equally in all directions and so a theoretical aerial called an isotropic source, i.e. one that radiates equally in all directions, is sometimes used. In this case the gain may be specified in dBi, i.e. gain in decibels over an isotropic source. If it ever becomes necessary to compare two figures for aerials which are specified in the two different ways simply taking 2.1 dB off the gain over an isotropic source will convert it to dB gain over a dipole.

Polarization
The basic idea of polarization has already been mentioned in Chapter 2. It is very important to know about it when dealing with aerials because the polarization of the aerial determines the polarization of the transmitted or received signal and this

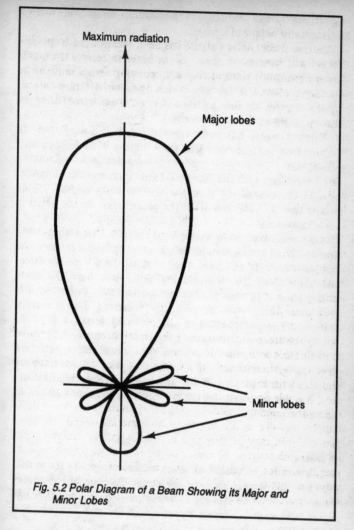

Fig. 5.2 Polar Diagram of a Beam Showing its Major and Minor Lobes

can often be very important.

For most aerials it is quite easy to determine the polarization. It is simply in the same plane as the elements of the aerial. So a vertical aerial will receive vertically polarized signals best and similarly a horizontal aerial will receive horizontally polarized signals.

In free space, once a signal has been transmitted its polarization will remain the same. So in order to receive the maximum signal both transmitting and receiving aerials must be in the same plane. If for any reason their polarizations are at ninety degrees to one another (i.e. cross polarized) then in theory no signal would be received.

Once a signal has been transmitted it is found that its polarization will remain the same unless it undergoes any reflections. For short range communications reflections from buildings and the like will tend to change the polarization of the overall signal at the receiver only slightly. This means that at VHF and UHF the polarization of the aerial is very important.

One everyday visual example of the fact that transmitting and receiving aerials should be the same can be seen on most houses today. It will be noticed that all the TV aerials directed at a given TV transmitting aerial will have the same polarization. In general they are horizontally polarized if it is a main transmitter or vertically polarized if it is a relay station. The polarization of the receiving aerials will all be set to the same polarization of the transmitter for best results.

For HF communications using the ionosphere, polarization is much less important. It is found that once a signal has been reflected back to earth it has an almost random polarization, and it is not necessary for the transmitting and receiving aerials to be the same.

Feeders

Many aerials are located at some distance from the set so that the best location is used for the aerial. To transfer the energy from the aerial to the set a feeder must be used. Although there are many different types of feeder the one which is universally used in scanner applications is coax.

The most common use around the home for coax is as a television or hi-fi aerial down lead. Essentially the coax consists of a centre conductor surrounded by an insulating dielectric. This is covered by a screening braid and then this has a protective plastic insulating layer over it as shown in Figure 5.3.

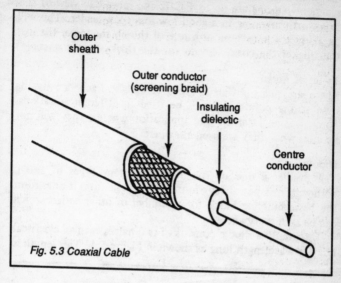

Fig. 5.3 Coaxial Cable

Coax comes in a variety of different types. Fortunately there is not a big problem in choosing the correct impedance parts for the aerial as there are some common standards. Television and hi-fi systems are designed to work on a 75 Ω standard. For professional communications, amateur radio and CB use 50 Ω. Scanners fall into the second category. There is no problem with the receivers themselves and specific scanner aerials as they will be designed for 50 Ω. However a little care is needed when buying coax. Normal television shops will only stock 75 Ω feeder so it will be necessary to go elsewhere. Scanner shops, CB dealers, amateur radio stockists and electronic component shops should all be able to supply 50 Ω cable, but be sure to specify the impedance.

The other point to note about coax is its loss. If only a very short run of coax is to be used then the loss of the coax may not be important. If any length is to be used then it can be quite significant and all the good work of erecting an efficient aerial and buying a good scanner can be put to waste.

The quality of the coax is made even more important by the fact that the loss of the cable rises with frequency and many scanners can operate up to 1 GHz and more. In view of this it is worth investing in a good low loss coax feeder. This will be fairly thick because as a rule of thumb the lower the loss the thicker the coax. So go for the thickest coax possible!

Types of Aerial
There are many different types of aerial. Each one has its own strong points and will be used in different situations. Some will be ideal for one application whereas they will not be ideal when they are used elsewhere.

Dipole
The dipole is one of the most important types of aerial. Although it is not always found in its basic form it does form the basic building block for a number of other aerials which can be seen everywhere.

Essentially a dipole consists of two halves each an electrical quarter wavelength long as shown in Figure 5.4. This length is

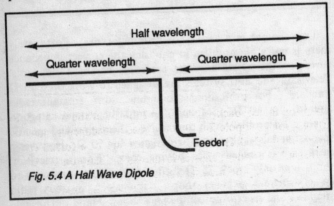

Fig. 5.4 A Half Wave Dipole

nearly the same as the wavelength of a signal in free space but it is slightly shorter because of a number of different effects. Although a dipole can be longer than half a wavelength, at frequencies above 30 MHz it is rarely used as anything but a half wave dipole. Each of these halves is then connected to the feeder.

When used on its own a dipole can perform well and it has a number of advantages. Probably the main one is its simplicity. It is quite easy to construct from two pieces of wire or rod. Also it is not too large and can be mounted externally without being too conspicuous.

On its own a dipole gives a good match to 75 Ω coax and can be made to operate quite acceptably with 50 Ω coax as well. However nearby objects can reduce the impedance of the aerial quite drastically, especially when it is used in conjunction with other elements in a more complicated aerial. To increase the impedance a folded dipole can be made as shown in Figure 5.5. This simply consists of the wire being

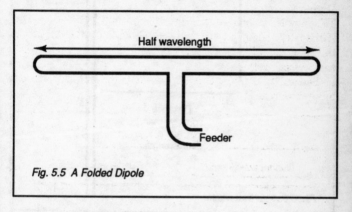

Fig. 5.5 A Folded Dipole

taken or folded back on itself and joined in the middle. By using a folded dipole like this the feed impedance is increased four fold to 300 Ω. The other advantage of a folded dipole is that it has a wider bandwidth than an ordinary one.

A dipole can be mounted either horizontally or vertically. For scanner use it is probably more likely to be used vertically. Like this it gives good all round coverage, but it should be mounted away from the mast as shown in Figure 5.6. If this is not done then the mast will adversely affect the operation of the aerial.

It is quite easy to construct a dipole. The simplest way is to use two pieces of wire cut to length. Each piece should be joined to the feeder as shown in Figure 5.7. To be absolutely

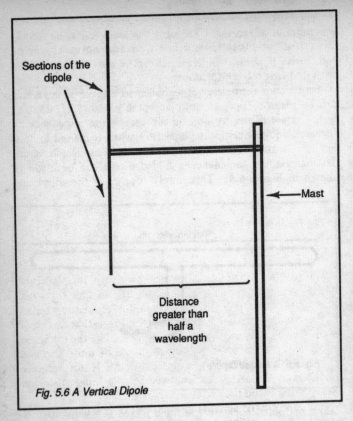

Fig. 5.6 A Vertical Dipole

correct a radio frequency transformer called a balun should be used between the aerial and the feeder if coax is used, but for most receiving purposes this is not absolutely necessary. The length for the wires can be determined from one of the formulae:

$$\text{Length (metres)} = \frac{147}{\text{Frequency (MHz)}}$$

$$\text{Length (inches)} = \frac{5785}{\text{Frequency (MHz)}}$$

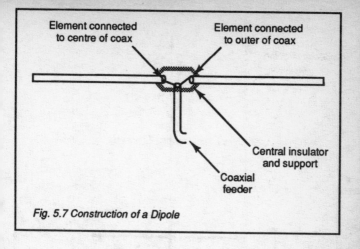

Fig. 5.7 Construction of a Dipole

The lengths which are calculated may vary slightly from the optimum lengths needed in practice. In fact they will become less accurate as the frequency increases, erring slightly on the long side. The reason for this is that the exact length will depend on a number of variables like the thickness of the wire. Even so these lengths should be quite accurate enough for most receiving purposes. If this is not accurate enough then the aerial can be made slightly longer than the required length and then trimmed to suit.

If a more robust aerial is needed for external use it may be possible to cannibalize an old 405 line television aerial. These aerials can often be found in attics and they can be in very good condition. Those which have been left outside are not likely to be of much use in view of their age. By using a spare aerial like this a cheap source of components can be obtained.

Yagi

In order to change the directional properties of a dipole it is possible to place other parasitic elements close to it. These extra elements interact with the signal in such a way that the aerial has more gain in a certain direction than another. Some elements tend to reflect the signal and are called reflectors

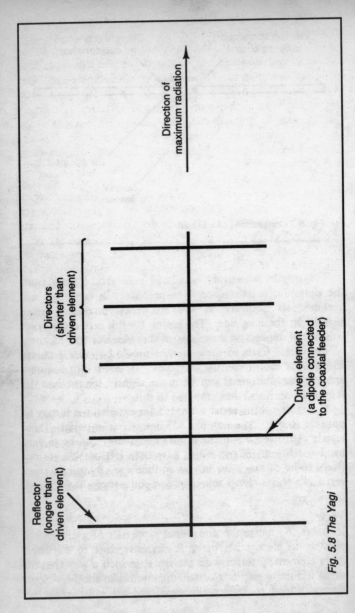

Direction of maximum radiation

Directors (shorter than driven element)

Driven element (a dipole connected to the coaxial feeder)

Reflector (longer than driven element)

Fig. 5.8 The Yagi

whilst others will direct the signal towards the dipole or driven element and are called directors.

The Yagi aerial is the most common directional aerial. In fact most television and VHF FM aerials are of this type. It is made up as shown in Figure 5.8. The reflector behind the driven element consists of a single rod about 5% longer than the dipole itself. Normally only one reflector is used as further ones do not make any noticeable difference. One or more directors can be placed in front of the driven element. The one nearest the driven element is about 5% shorter than the dipole and any further ones are slightly shorter still.

The spacing between the elements is generally about a quarter to three-eighths of a wavelength. This spacing is normally not very critical and is adjusted to give the correct impedance. However, as the presence of the extra elements does reduce the impedance of the dipole by quite an extent, a folded dipole is normally employed for the driven element. This brings the impedance up to a more convenient value.

Discone

The discone is probably the most popular aerial amongst scanner enthusiasts. This is because it has a very wide bandwidth often extending over a range of as much as 10 : 1.

The aerial has a very distinctive shape as shown in Figure 5.9. From this it can be seen that it is made up from wire elements which form a disc at the top with a cone below it. It is because of these two shapes that it receives its name.

The aerial achieves its wide bandwidth because of its unusual shape. The number of elements is not particularly critical, but the more that are used the better the performance because it simulates the shapes more effectively. However, as the number of elements rises so does the wind resistance and the cost. Normally six or eight elements are used as a suitable compromise.

The size of the aerial is governed by the lowest frequency which is required. The cone should be about a quarter of a wavelength in diameter at the lowest frequency whilst the disc should have a diameter of about 0.175 of a wavelength.

The aerial is vertically polarized and matches 50 Ω quite well. However it is seldom used for transmitting because it is

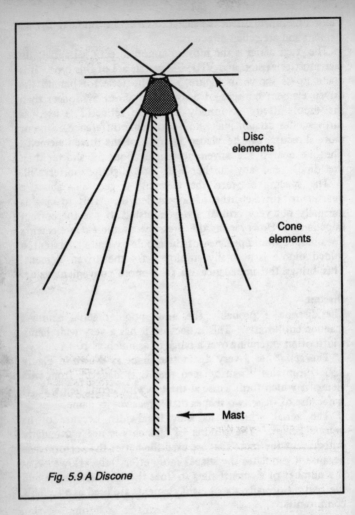

Disc elements

Cone elements

← Mast

Fig. 5.9 A Discone

not very efficient, having traded efficiency for bandwidth.

Vertical

Vertical aerials appear in many forms and have become popular for a number of reasons. The first is that they are robust and easy to make. Also they have an omnidirectional or all

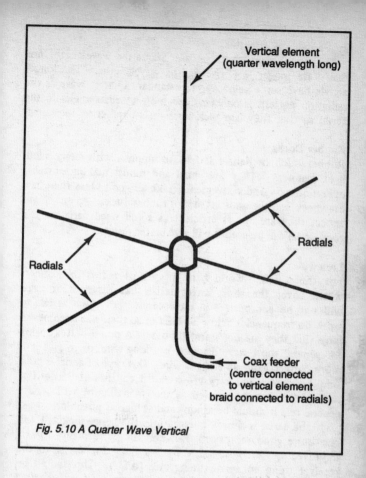

Fig. 5.10 A Quarter Wave Vertical

round radiation pattern. They also have a low angle of radiation which makes them more sensitive to ground stations as signals will arrive parallel to the earth.

The simplest form of vertical can be likened to a vertical half wave dipole. The top half of the dipole is used in the conventional form whereas the bottom section is removed and replaced by a ground plane as shown in Figure 5.10. The ground plane is ideally made from an infinite metal sheet but in practice a number of quarter wave radials or even a car roof are just as effective.

Although many verticals are a quarter wavelength long many are longer, e.g. five-eighths wavelengths. The longer aerials have some gain over the standard quarter wave as the radiation pattern is concentrated more at right angles to the aerial so that they can pick up signals parallel to the earth.

Rubber Ducks

Rubber duck or helical aerials are supplied with many hand-held scanners. They are small and robust making portable operation easy and convenient. Like all good ideas there is a drawback and the same is true for rubber ducks. As one might expect they are not as efficient as a full sized aerial so if a good aerial can be used it will give better results.

Longwire

For those with "world band" types of radios or scanners which cover the short waves aerials like discones or yagis will not be appropriate in most cases. For these aerials to work on frequencies below 30 MHz or so their size becomes so large that they are not normally used. A much better option for general short wave listening is a long wire, or to give it is more correct name an end fed wire. This type of aerial is both simple to erect and very effective. It consists of a length of wire and it can be erected as shown in Figure 5.11. As a general rule it should be as long and as high as possible.

If the aerial is simply plugged into the aerial socket it will give quite good reception. However the performance can be improved quite considerably by matching the aerial to the receiver using an aerial tuning unit (ATU). This should be fitted into the system as shown in Figure 5.12. There is a good variety of these units on the market. Many of them are quite expensive, but if it is only to be used for receiving then this will reduce the cost of the unit which is needed quite considerably.

In addition to an ATU a good earth will bring some improvements. Just using the mains earth will mean that plenty of general electrical noise will be introduced into the aerial system. It is much better to use a separate earth for the

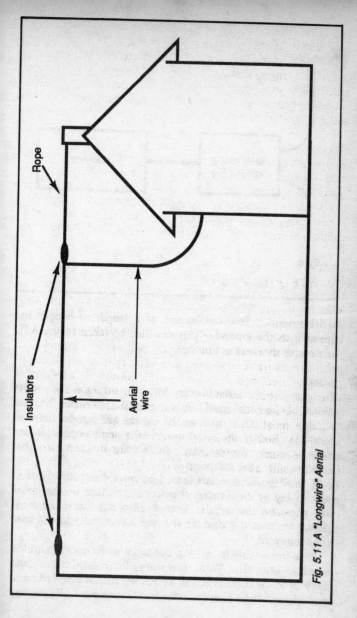

Rope

Insulators

Aerial wire

Fig. 5.11 A "Longwire" Aerial

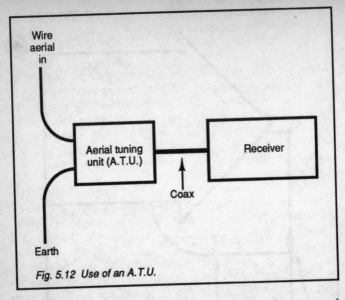

Fig. 5.12 Use of an A.T.U.

aerial system. This can consist of a length of copper rod driven into the ground. This can then be taken to the ATU using as short a lead as possible.

Siting
The siting of the aerial is every bit as important as the correct choice of the aerial itself. If it is poorly sited then it will not be able to perform well as the signals will not be there to pick up! Ideally the aerial should be as high as possible and away from any obstructions. In fact the better view it has then the better the reception.

If at all possible aerials should be erected outside. Particularly at higher frequencies the actual structure of the house will attenuate the signals. Even so all is not lost if the aerial cannot be located outside, but lower signal strengths will have to be tolerated.

It is also advisable to keep the aerial as far away from the house as possible. With televisions, fluorescent lights, and many other appliances in the house, significant levels of noise can be generated which can mask out some signals. By moving the aerial away from the house the noise level can be reduced by a considerable extent.

Installation

When installing the aerial safety must be borne in mind all the time. The proper fittings and fixings should always be used and they should not be over stressed by placing too large an aerial on them. Remember that the force on an aerial caused by wind resistance can be quite large. Also the weather can be quite corrosive over long periods of time. Remember this because it can be dangerous and not a little embarrassing if an aerial collapses.

Aerials should be mounted so that people cannot injure themselves on them. Whilst most aerials are well out of reach, sometimes guy wires or lengths of feeder may get in the way. Adequate attention must be paid to ensure this is not a problem.

Finally aerials should not be mounted near any power cables. People have been killed on a number of occasions when aerials have fallen onto these cables. Apart from this these cables are likely to be a source of a lot of interference.

Chapter 6

THE RADIO SPECTRUM

Scanner operation is normally associated with frequencies between about 30 MHz and 1300 MHz. However with new scanners being launched onto the market their coverage is being extended quite considerably. In particular many new receivers are able to cover frequencies below 30 MHz giving them the capability of covering a very varied selection of bands.

Frequency Designations

The radio spectrum covers a very large portion of the electro-magnetic spectrum. It extends from below a few kilohertz right up to many thousands of Megahertz. At the low end of the spectrum below 100 kHz there are a number of stations which are transmitting. One is the standard frequency transmission from MSF at Rugby in England. In addition to this there are a number of navigational stations and some maritime communications. Then at the other end of the spectrum semiconductors are being produced which have lower noise levels or higher output powers at frequencies of over 100 GHz (100,000 MHz). These developments mean that these higher frequencies will be more widely used in the future.

In view of the fact that the radio spectrum is so wide, different frequency bands are given designations as shown in Figure 6.1. This makes referring to different frequency bands much easier. Within these bands there are many familiar services. For example the MF band contains the medium wave broadcast transmissions. Then the HF portion of the spectrum carries the long distance communications which use the ionospheric reflections to propagate around the world. The VHF band carries the FM broadcasts between 87.5 and 108 MHz. The next portion of the spectrum carries the 625 line terrestrial television services like BBC1, BBC2 and ITV. The frequencies extend up well beyond this into the SHF and EHF

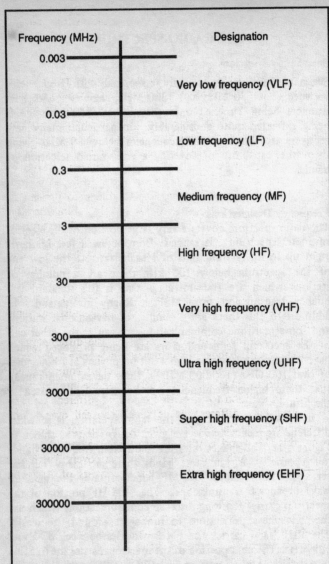

Fig. 6.1 Designation of the Radio Spectrum

regions and carry a wide variety of different transmissions, including the new satellite television transmissions around 12 GHz.

Spectrum Allocations

Apart from the transmissions like television and radio broadcasts which are well known, the airwaves carry a whole host of other transmissions. Everything from small radio pagers to large radar installations appear somewhere in the spectrum. If all of these transmissions were allowed to go unchecked, picking frequencies where they wanted without any regard for other users then chaos would reign because levels of interference would be very high. In order to overcome this state of affairs careful planning is undertaken to prevent it. In fact international conferences (World Administrative Radio Conferences or WARC for short) are held every few years so that world wide agreements can be drawn up. This needs to be done on an international basis because radio communications cross national boundaries. This is obviously true on the HF bands where signals can travel very great distances. However agreements are also needed at higher frequencies where satellite services also cross national boundaries.

To regulate the different services, all the different users are given specific bands in which they can operate. Obviously there are some differences between different countries, but these are organised in such a way that no undue interference is caused. In addition to this it is found that different areas of the world have different needs which can fall outside the normal limits which can be normally catered for. To overcome this the world is split up into three regions. Region 1 covers Europe, CIS and Africa; Region 2 covers North and South America; and finally Region 3 consists of Asia and Oceania.

Figure 6.2 gives an outline of the different bands which are allocated. In some instances some users will have to share a band whereas in others they are allocated exclusively for a particular use.

From the table it can be seen that there are a great number of users as well as a vast amount of spectrum space which is

MHz

0.100 −	0.1405	Fixed; Maritime Mobile; Radionavigation
0.1405 −	0.2835	Broadcast (Region 1)
0.2835 −	0.415	Radionavigation
0.415 −	0.495	Maritime Mobile
0.495 −	0.505	Mobile distress and calling
0.505 −	0.5265	Aeronautical Radionavigation; Maritime Mobile
0.5265 −	1.6065	Broadcast
1.6065 −	1.625	Fixed; Mobile; Maritime Mobile
1.625 −	1.635	Radiolocation
1.635 −	1.800	Fixed; Mobile; Maritime Mobile
1.800 −	1.810	Radiolocation
1.810 −	1.850	Amateur (Region 2 & 3 have an allocation down to 1.800)
1.850 −	2.000	Amateur
1.850 −	2.045	Fixed; Mobile
2.045 −	2.160	Fixed; Maritime Mobile
2.160 −	2.170	Radiolocation
2.170 −	2.1735	Maritime Mobile
2.1735 −	2.1905	Mobile (Distress and calling)
2.1905 −	2.194	Maritime
2.194 −	2.625	Fixed; Mobile inc. Maritime Mobile
2.300 −	2.498	Broadcast (Tropical Band only)
2.498 −	2.502	Standard Frequency
2.625 −	2.650	Maritime Mobile
2.650 −	2.850	Fixed; Mobile
2.850 −	3.155	Aeronautical Mobile
3.155 −	3.400	Fixed; Mobile
3.200 −	3.400	Broadcast
3.400 −	3.500	Aeronautical Mobile
3.500 −	3.800	Amateur; Fixed; Mobile
3.800 −	4.000	Amateur (Region 2)
3.800 −	3.900	Amateur (Region 3)
3.800 −	3.900	Fixed; Aeronautical Mobile; Mobile
3.850 −	3.950	Aeronautical Mobile

Fig. 6.2 Summary of Frequency Allocations in Region 1

MHz		
3.950 – 4.000	Broadcast; Fixed
4.000 – 4.063	Fixed; Maritime Mobile
4.063 – 4.438	Maritime Mobile
4.438 – 4.650	Fixed; Mobile
4.650 – 4.750	Aeronautical Mobile
4.750 – 4.995	Broadcast; Fixed; Mobile
4.995 – 5.005	Standard Frequency and Time Signal
5.005 – 5.060	Broadcast; Fixed
5.060 – 5.480	Fixed; Mobile
5.450 – 5.480	Fixed; Aeronautical Mobile; Mobile
5.480 – 5.730	Aeronautical Mobile
5.730 – 5.950	Fixed; Mobile
5.950 – 6.200	Broadcast
6.200 – 6.525	Maritime Mobile
6.525 – 6.765	Aeronautical Mobile
6.765 – 7.000	Fixed; Mobile
7.000 – 7.100	Amateur
7.100 – 7.300	Amateur (Region 2 only); Broadcast (Regions 1 and 2)
7.300 – 8.100	Fixed; Mobile
8.100 – 8.195	Fixed
8.100 – 8.815	Maritime Mobile
8.815 – 9.040	Aeronautical Mobile
9.040 – 9.500	Fixed
9.500 – 9.900	Broadcast
9.900 – 9.995	Fixed
9.995 – 10.005	Standard Frequency and Time Signal
10.005 – 10.100	Aeronautical Mobile
10.100 – 10.150	Amateur
10.100 – 10.175	Fixed
10.175 – 11.400	Aeronautical Mobile
11.400 – 11.650	Fixed
11.650 – 12.050	Broadcast
12.050 – 12.230	Fixed

Fig. 6.2 Continued

MHz

12.230	− 13.200	Maritime Mobile
13.200	− 13.360	Aeronautical Mobile
13.360	− 13.600	Fixed
13.600	− 13.800	Broadcast
13.800	− 14.000	Fixed
14.000	− 14.350	Amateur
14.350	− 14.990	Fixed
14.990	− 15.010	Standard Frequency and Time Signal
15.010	− 15.100	Aeronautical Mobile
15.100	− 15.600	Broadcast
15.600	− 16.360	Fixed
16.360	− 17.410	Maritime Mobile
17.410	− 17.550	Fixed
17.550	− 17.900	Broadcast
17.900	− 18.030	Aeronautical Mobile
18.030	− 18.068	Fixed
18.068	− 18.168	Amateur
18.168	− 18.780	Fixed
18.780	− 18.900	Maritime Mobile
18.900	− 19.680	Fixed
19.680	− 19.800	Maritime Mobile
19.800	− 19.990	Fixed
19.990	− 20.010	Standard Frequency and Time Signal
20.010	− 21.000	Fixed; Mobile
21.000	− 21.450	Amateur
21.450	− 21.850	Broadcast
21.850	− 21.870	Fixed
21.870	− 21.924	Aeronautical Fixed
21.924	− 22.000	Aeronautical Mobile
22.000	− 22.855	Maritime Mobile
22.855	− 23.200	Fixed; Mobile
23.200	− 23.350	Aeronautical Fixed; Aeronautical Mobile
23.350	− 24.890	Fixed; Mobile

Fig. 6.2 Continued

72

MHz		
24.890 – 24.990	Amateur	
24.990 – 25.010	Standard Frequency and Time Signal	
25.010 – 25.070	Fixed; Mobile	
25.070 – 25.210	Maritime Mobile	
25.210 – 25.550	Fixed; Mobile	
25.550 – 25.670	Radio Astronomy	
25.670 – 26.100	Broadcast	
26.100 – 26.175	Maritime Mobile	
26.175 – 28.000	Fixed; Mobile	
27.500 – 28.000	Meteorological Aids	
28.000 – 29.700	Amateur	
29.700 – 30.000	Fixed; Mobile	
30.00 – 50.00	Fixed; Mobile	
47.00 – 68.00	Broadcast (TV)	
50.00 – 54.00	Amateur (Regions 2 and 3. Some countries in Region 1 inc. UK have an amateur allocation between 50.00 and 52.00)	
54.00 – 72.00	Broadcast (Regions 2 and 3)	
68.00 – 74.80	Fixed; Mobile	
74.80 – 75.20	Aeronautical Radionavigation	
75.20 – 87.50	Fixed; Mobile	
87.50 – 108.00	Broadcast (FM)	
108.00 – 117.975	Aeronautical Radionavigation	
117.975 – 137.00	Aeronautical Mobile	
137.00 – 138.00	Space Operation; Meteorological Satellite; Space Research	
138.00 – 144.00	Aeronautical Mobile	
143.60 – 143.65	Space Research	
144.00 – 146.00	Amateur	
146.00 – 148.00	Amateur (Regions 2 and 3)	
146.00 – 149.90	Fixed; Mobile	
149.90 – 150.05	Radionavigation (Satellite)	
150.05 – 156.7625	Fixed; Mobile	
156.7625 – 156.8375	Maritime Mobile (Distress and Calling)	

Fig. 6.2 Continued

MHz		
156.8375	− 174.00	Fixed; Mobile
174.00	− 230.00	Broadcast (TV)
230.00	− 328.60	Fixed; Mobile
272.00	− 273.00	Space Operation
328.60	− 335.40	Aeronautical Navigation
328.60	− 335.40	Aeronautical Radionavigation
335.40	− 399.90	Fixed; Mobile
399.90	− 400.05	Radionavigation (Satellite)
400.05	− 400.15	Standard Frequency and Time Signal based on a frequency of 400.10 MHz)
400.00	− 410.00	Meteorology; Space Research
410.00	− 430.00	Fixed; Mobile
430.00	− 440.00	Amateur; Radiolocation
440.00	− 470.00	Fixed; Mobile
470.00	− 790.00	Broadcast
790.00	− 862.00	Fixed; Broadcast
862.00	− 960.00	Fixed; Mobile; Broadcast
960.00	− 1215.00	Aeronautical Radionavigation
1215.00	− 1240.00	Radiolocation; Radionavigation (Satellite)
1240.00	− 1300.00	Radiolocation; Amateur

Fig. 6.2 Continued

allocated. Broadcasting, amateur radio, and citizen's band are described in further detail in other chapters. Other users are briefly outlined here for interest but it should be noted that it is not legal to listen to them in the UK.

Designations
The different designations given to the different types of users cover a very wide range of users. This allows the governments in the different countries a large degree of discretion in what they want to use these bands for, but

74

without the risk of interference to users in other countries. Obviously there must be a large degree of agreement and standardisation over users such as aeronautical mobile and maritime mobile as these transmissions are likely to be international by the nature of the aircraft and seagoing vessels. Also the different forms of space and satellite transmissions will cross national boundaries. However, fixed stations and land mobile transmissions, especially if they are in the VHF or UHF portion of the spectrum, are unlikely to cause undue interference to neighbouring countries. As a result allocations for services like CB, car phones, cell phones, pagers and a host of other users all come into this category.

Private Mobile Radio (PMR)
This type of communication is widely used for small businesses like taxis, as well as the larger ones. It is used for maintaining communications between a base station and a number of mobile or remote stations. PMR systems may either be a simple simplex system or they may be half or full duplex. There are a number of different bands allocated to this type of service within the VHF and UHF portions of the spectrum. Some use AM but the majority use FM these days.

Car Phones
This service is a first generation type of mobile phone. It is not particularly sophisticated by today's standards having several distinct limitations but it does enable phone calls to be made from cars. However the range is limited and only certain cities are covered.

Cell Phones
The rise in popularity of cell phones has been quite phenomenal since their introduction in the 1980s. The two UK operators, Vodafone and Cellnet, have found their systems have been so well adopted because of their convenience. It is possible to make and receive calls in most places within the country.

Essentially cell phones are a very sophisticated form of car phone. They operate by splitting the country up into small areas called cells, each one is covered by its own base station.

This base station handles all the phones in its area at any given time. When a phone moves from one cell into the next this is detected by the system and the call is automatically routed through to the next base station. As all the base stations are linked to one another the call can be continued without interruption when the phone passes from one cell to the next, and continuous coverage is achieved.

These systems all use FM because it gives better performance in view of the fact that most of the stations are mobile.

Paging Systems

This service also comes under the umbrella of a fixed station. There are two main types of pager. The first is a low power system for on site use. The second is called wide area paging.

In general any paging system is a one way transmission. A base station transmits a signal which is picked up by all the pagers in the system. However only one pager will be activated because the signal will be coded and carry information to address only one pager.

Different paging systems are able to give different levels of service. In the simplest form they just give a bleep to alert the owner. Other more sophisticated systems can give a short message which is displayed on the pager.

Marine Communications

Radio communication between ships and shore or coastal stations, and from one ship to another is vital. It is used for everything from the captains of large ocean going cargo vessels informing their companies when they are going to arrive in a particular port, to small craft passing messages to one another. Then there is the very important aspect where radio carries distress calls. In this way radio has saved many thousands of lives over the years and this is likely to continue well into the future.

In view of the fact that there are thousands of vessels on the oceans it is necessary to organise the use of the frequency allocations to prevent confusion.

On the VHF marine band narrowband FM is used and a range of 20 or 30 miles can be achieved. Operation is channelized and these channels are recognized internationally.

Some channels are simplex whilst others are for duplex operation. For duplex operation one frequency is allocated for the coastal stations transmissions whilst the other is used by the ship.

One channel is designated as a calling channel. This is used to call up another station. Having established contact they move to an agreed channel. In addition the calling channel is also used for distress calls and when coastal stations need to give notice of weather or other special announcements to be made on another channel.

Using this form of system means that stations only have to monitor a single channel. This is particularly important as it makes calling a particular coastal station or vessel much easier.

When communication is required over greater distances the MF or HF bands are used. Here too operation is channelized, but instead of using narrowband FM, other modes including radio telex, SSB and morse are used. Channels are still used on the HF bands. In the new channel system which is being adopted, one frequency is allocated to the coastal station and the other to the ship for each channel. This enables full duplex to be used if necessary. Calling channels are designed and used in the same way that they are on VHF.

There are a number of different HF bands which are available. This variety of different bands is needed because the nature of the ionosphere means that communications may be possible on one band but not on another.

In the MF portion of the spectrum operation tends to be a little different. Many coastal stations are allocated a channel or a number of channels which they use. There is also a distress and calling frequency. This is kept free of all calls at certain times to allow any weak distress calls to be heard.

With the advance of technology the more traditional LF, MF and HF communications for long distances are giving way to a much greater use of satellite communications. This provides a much better medium for passing all communications. It is far more reliable because it does not rely on the ionosphere with its changes. There is also much less interference and this means that the quality of the links is much better.

Callsigns

Stations are issued with callsigns which are used particularly on morse. On SSB it is more usual for the vessel's name or the coastal station's name to be used. Callsigns for ships consist of four letters. From this it is possible to determine the country of origin of the vessel by comparing it with the ITU prefixes given in Appendix II. For example, GZZZ would be registered in the UK. Coastal or shore stations are allocated callsigns with three letters. Sometimes coastal station callsigns may have some numbers after the letters, e.g. GZZ12. This is sometimes done when several stations are linked together in some way or another.

Aeronautical Communications

The need for communications between aircraft and ground stations has grown rapidly with the increase in air traffic over recent years. This form of communication is vital because air traffic is controlled in a highly organized manner to ensure that accidents are reduced to a minimum level. To accommodate all the required communication a large amount of spectrum is required both in the HF and VHF portions of the spectrum.

Protocol

Control towers and air traffic controllers may need to communicate with a large number of craft at any given time. In order to be able to identify each aircraft callsigns are allocated. These are marked on the outside of the craft and consist of five letters. These callsigns have two sections: the prefix and the serial letters. The prefix will be in accordance with the ITU prefix allocations given in Appendix II. From this it is possible to determine the aircraft's country of origin. For example, if the prefix was G-PQRS then the aircraft would come from the UK, whereas one with the callsign or registration N-TUVW would come from the USA.

These callsigns are always used by light aircraft. However commercial aircraft use a different system. Although they are allocated callsigns it is more usual for the company and flight number to be used for radio communications. This is done because it is possible to find out items like the destination and normal flight time.

Frequencies

Aircraft need to talk to a number of different ground stations during the course of the flight. To enable the aircraft to be able to select which station it wants to talk to each station is allocated one or more frequencies. This means that to call a specific station the craft will switch to the relevant frequency to make the call.

For communications a number of different bands are used. For short range communications of a few miles the VHF band is used. For example, control towers and most air traffic control use this band on AM and operation is simplex. There may also be some FM communications here as well but this is mainly very short range communications for ground support services in the airport.

Longer range communications like the craft trying to communicate over several thousand miles will either use HF or possibly satellites now. HF communicatiõns will use SSB. Ground stations will be allocated a number of different frequencies so that the aircraft can call on the specific frequency allocated to a particular station. However, to accommodate the changes in the ionosphere each ground station will need a number of different frequencies.

Volmets

Volmets or meteos are used for giving continuous weather reports, and they use both the HF and VHF bands. By using both portions of the spectrum it is possible to receive both local and international reports. This means that it is possible for an aircraft to receive exact reports about where it is about to land or a long distance destination.

Another similar service is called an ATIS or automated terminal information service. It contains information about its specific airport. This will include weather and wind conditions as well as the runway and approach patterns.

Aeronautical Radionavigation

There are a number of navigational aids which are available to aircraft. They are often referred to by their abbreviations.

The main ones are: NDB (Non-Directional Beacon); VOR (VHF Omni Range); and DME (Distance Measuring Equipment).

NDB: Non-directional beacons have been in use for a long time. Despite this they are still widely used, transmitting in the air navigational bands between the long and medium wave broadcast bands. Their transmissions are broadcast equally in all directions and have a morse identification on their signals. The actual direction finding is performed in the aircraft itself where an aerial is rotated to located the heading of the signal.

VOR: This type of navigational aid is used by aircraft to give them bearings. The beacons are set up at a number of sites around the country, having a range of up to 200 miles or more. In this way aircraft are able to obtain bearings from specific points around the country.

VOR beacons transmit in the air navigational band between 109 and 117.975 MHz. They operate by transmitting two types of signal. The first rotates around the beacon in a clockwise direction at 30 revolutions per second. The second is a reference signal transmitted in all directions and is modulated by a 30 Hz sine wave. When an aircraft is due north of the beacon the two signals appear to be in phase. However, as the aircraft moves away from north towards the east a phase difference appears between the two. This phase difference corresponds to the bearing away from north. Thus it is a relatively simple matter for the electronics in the aircraft to indicate the bearing of the aircraft from the beacon.

DME: These units are normally located at the same site as a VOR beacon. Essentially they enable the aircraft to determine the distance it is away from the DME unit. By knowing the bearing and the distance from the VOR/DME station it is possible for the aircraft to obtain its exact location.

Their basis of operation is quite simple. An aircraft sends out a signal to the DME station which is then retransmitted back to the aircraft. By measuring the time interval between sending and receiving the signal it is possible to determine the distance to the DME station.

In practice there has to be a frequency difference between the transmitted and received signal. This is normally 63 MHz. Also each DME station will have its own frequency. Therefore it is possible to identify a particular DME station by its frequency.

If several aircraft are using the same DME station then it is possible for confusion to occur because the receiver will not know if it is receiving its returned signal or one from another aircraft. To overcome this problem a series of pulses is transmitted. Only when the received pulse train exactly matches the one the aircraft transmitted will the distance be calculated.

Standard Frequency and Time Signals

At a number of different places in the spectrum signals with very accurate frequencies are transmitted. The most commonly known are those on 2.5, 5.0, 10.0, 15.0 and 20.0 MHz, although other frequencies are used. Apart from giving a very accurate frequency measurement these signals also carry time information. This is generally in the form of some "pips" similar to those on the national broadcast services. A list of the main stations is given in Figure 6.3 below.

Country & Location	Callsign	Frequencies (MHz)
Argentina - Buenos Aires	LOL	5.000, 10.000, 15.000
Australia - Lyndhurst	VNG	4.500, 7.500, 12.000
Canada - Ottawa	CHU	3.330, 7.335, 14.670
France - Paris	FFH	2.500
Japan - Tokyo	JJY	2.500, 5.000, 10.000, 15.000
USA - Ft Collins, Col.	WWV	2.500, 5.000, 10.000, 15.000, 20.000
USA - Kauai, Hawaii	WWVH	2.500, 5.000, 10.000, 15.000
USSR - Moscow	RWM	4.996, 9.996, 14.996
USSR - Irkutsk	RID	5.004, 10.004, 15.004
South Africa - Pretoria	ZUO	2.500, 5.000

Fig. 6.3 Standard Frequency Transmissions

Signals on these standard frequencies are not always radiated continually because several stations have to share the same frequencies. As identification these transmissions use morse to give their callsigns, usually at the beginning of each period of transmission. Thereafter the time pips are transmitted.

When listening to these transmissions beware of the Russian station RWM which can be heard very easily in the UK. It transmits just below the round frequencies to alleviate interference. As it is 4 kHz low it might give rise to some concern about the receiver accuracy if it was picked up.

Like broadcast stations and amateur radio no licence is required in the UK to receive these transmissions.

Chapter 7

GENERAL OPERATING PROCEDURES

The way in which people talk over a communications radio link may seem rather formal and unnatural. However, good operating procedures and techniques are very important. They can save time and enable contact to be maintained far more easily when interference levels rise or signals are not very strong.

Whilst different users will have slightly different techniques there are many strands which are common to many radio users. Often codes may be used by many different people or there are techniques which have been proved over years of experience.

Operating Techniques

One of the basic requirements for any radio operator is that messages should be short and precise. By doing this the person at the other end knows exactly what the message is. In addition to this the channel is kept open longer for other users.

Operating procedure is particularly important when using simplex links. It is vitally important for the operators at either end of the link to know what the other intends to do. For example, it is necessary to say when one is passing transmission to the other. As a result words like "over" and so forth are used. Although this may all sound a little bit cumbersome it can become very confusing if neither end knows what the other one is doing and both stations end up transmitting at the same time.

Phonetic Alphabet

When mentioning letters over the air it is found that it is quite easy for them to be confused. Letters like "c" and "t" are a good example. In fact it is quite easy for a large number of letters to be confused with one another, especially when signal levels are low or there is some interference. In order to overcome this problem a phonetic alphabet has been introduced to help identify each letter. Although there are a few different phonetic alphabets which have been developed over the years the one which is standard is given in Figure 7.1.

A	Alpha	N	November
B	Bravo	O	Oscar
C	Charlie	P	Papa
D	Delta	Q	Quebec
E	Echo	R	Romeo
F	Foxtrot	S	Sierra
G	Golf	T	Tango
H	Hotel	U	Uniform
I	India	V	Victor
J	Juliet	W	Whisky
K	Kilo	X	X-Ray
L	Lima	Y	Yankee
M	Mike	Z	Zulu

Fig. 7.1 Phonetic Alphabet

Other Expressions
In common with almost any other subject there are a number of words or expressions which take on a special meaning over the air. Many of these expressions are in fact used by a large number of radio users.

Q Code
There are a number of other codes which are used. Sometimes these codes will only be used by one particular service, whereas some others are used by a number of different groups. One example of a code which appears in a number of different areas is the Q Code. It was first devised in the early days of radio and it soon became standard for a whole host of users including ships, aircraft, and amateur radio. In fact its use is so widespread that the meanings are defined by an international body called the International Telecommunications Union which lays down international regulations for the

Mayday   This is an internationally recognised distress
         call. It is generally used for voice communi-
         cations whereas SOS is used for morse.

Over   This means that the transmission is being passed
         over to the other station. This is important
         because it lets the other stations know exactly
         when he can start to transmit.

Roger   This means that the message has been
         understood.

Wilco   This means that the station who has just
         received the message will do as they have
         been asked.

Fig. 7.2 General Expressions

QRA   What is the name of your station?
      The name of my station is . . . .

QRB   How far are you from my station?
      I am about . . . . from your station.

QRG   What is my exact frequency?
      My exact frequency is . . . .

QRH   Does my frequency vary?
      Your frequency varies.

QRI   Does the note of my transmission vary?
      Your note varies.

QRJ   Is my signal weak?
      Your signal is weak.

Fig. 7.3 Q Codes

QRK	What is the readability of my signal? The readability of your signal is . . . .
QRL	Are you busy? I am busy.
QRM	Is there any (man made) interference? There is (man made) interference.
QRN	Is there any atmospheric noise? There is atmospheric noise.
QRO	Shall I increase power? Increase power.
QRP	Shall I decrease power? Decrease power.
QRQ	Shall I send faster? Send faster.
QRS	Shall I send more slowly? Send more slowly.
QRT	Shall I stop sending? Stop sending.
QRU	Do you have any messages for me? I have no messages for you.
QRV	Are you ready to receive? I am ready to receive.
QRZ	Who is calling me? You are being called by . . . .
QSK	Can you hear between your signals? i.e. use break in on morse transmissions. I can hear between my signals.

Fig. 7.3 Continued

QSL	Can you acknowledge receipt? I can acknowledge receipt.
QSP	Can you relay a message? I can relay a message.
QSV	Shall I send a series of Vs? Send a series of Vs.
QSY	Shall I change to another frequency? Change to another frequency.
QTH	What is your location? My location is . . . .
QTR	What is the exact time? The exact time is . . . .

Fig. 7.3 Continued

use of the radio spectrum. There is a very large number of Q codes and the ones which are more common are given in Figure 7.3.

It can be seen from the table that the Q codes themselves are in the form of questions and answers. Their actual meaning is then dependent upon the way in which they are used.

In amateur radio these codes are sometimes used a little differently. For example, an amateur may say he has a QRO transmitter, meaning that he has a high power transmitter. Also the code QTH strictly means the location in terms of latitude and longitude whereas radio amateurs tend to use it to denote their address.

Time

All radio operators use the 24-hour clock. It is far easier to use and saves a lot of confusion over the standard 12-hour clock. Thus 4 o'clock in the afternoon becomes 16.00 hrs which is often pronounced sixteen hundred hours.

A base line is also needed because different places around the world will be at different times. In general Greenwich Mean Time (GMT) is used as the base and all other times are referred to it. As a result of its universal use it is sometimes called Coordinated Universal Time (abbreviated UTC from its French equivalent). Alternatively, times in GMT may be specified as the time with a Z (or Zulu) after the figures, e.g. 16.00 Z is the same as 16.00 GMT.

Chapter 8

BROADCASTING

Listening to broadcast stations on all of the different bands can be a very interesting aspect to scanning. Not only are there a great number of local stations which can be heard, but it is also possible to hear a very wide variety of stations from all over the world on the short wave bands which many scanners cover today. In fact many scanners give the choice of listening to stations on the Long Wave, Medium Wave and VHF FM Band as well as those on the Short Waves and television bands. This gives a tremendous variety for the listener.

The more traditional form of listening is undertaken on the Long, Medium and Short Waves. The bands within this portion of the spectrum are shown in Figure 8.1. However, there is just as much, if not more, to hear further up the spectrum at VHF and UHF.

Long Wave	0.150	–	0.285
Medium Wave	0.5265	–	1.6065
120 Metres	2.300	–	2.498
90 Metres	3.200	–	3.400
75 Metres	3.950	–	4.000
60 Metres	4.750	–	5.060
49 Metres	5.950	–	6.200
41 Metres	7.100	–	7.300
31 Metres	9.500	–	9.900
25 Metres	11.650	–	12.050
22 Metres	13.600	–	13.800
19 Metres	15.100	–	15.600
16 Metres	17.550	–	17.900
13 Metres	21.450	–	21.850
11 Metres	25.670	–	26.100

All frequencies are in MHz

Fig. 8.1 Long, Medium and Short Wave Broadcast Bands

Long and Medium Wave Bands

The long and medium wave bands are where the local and national broadcast services are transmitted. Generally the long wave has high power stations like the BBC Radio 4 transmitter at Droitwich which can cover most of the UK and can be heard well into France and other parts of Europe. The medium wave band does not have as wide a coverage as the long wave. Services like the BBC Radio 1, Radio 3 and Radio 5 transmissions need several transmitters to cover the country. In addition to this it is used for the BBC and independent local radio services. The medium wave is ideal for these transmissions as they only need to cover a comparatively small area and this can be accomplished using fairly low power transmitters. Some of the local transmitters only transmit a few hundred watts whilst some of the larger network service transmitters for Radio 1 and 5 use many kilowatts.

Even though the long and medium wave bands are not normally associated with listening for distant stations it is surprising what can be heard. At night time propagation improves on both bands although it is much more marked on the medium wave. When this happens, interference levels rise as more stations are picked up. However, with some careful listening it is possible to pick out a very large number of stations. In fact it is not difficult to receive stations up to 1500 km distance. Some people even listen in the very early hours when many of the large transmitters are switched off to conserve power. This drastically reduces interference levels and weaker signals from stations even three or four thousand km away can be heard.

Broadcasting on the long and medium wave bands is on AM and the channel spacing is 9 kHz.

Short Wave Broadcasting

It is on the short waves that the biggest variety of stations can be heard. Stations from all over the world can be received quite easily without the need for special receiving aerials. These stations can be in almost any language but with English being spoken by a large number of countries it is not difficult to hear and understand a good selection of stations.

Short wave stations have a very wide variety of programmes. Often they are intended to be the mouthpiece for their country and they carry the government's point of view. This makes listening to them interesting and also quite educational. In addition to the political and news programmes which are heard, these stations also transmit programmes about their country which can also be very interesting. In addition to this these stations carry music and other general programmes. As they have to work hard to gain their audiences, the standard of programmes which are broadcast is usually quite high. For example, the BBC World Service is renowned for the quality of its broadcasts and in particular its news service.

Although it may be thought that short wave broadcasting is likely to be on the decline with all the new technology which is available now, nothing could be further from the truth. Governments see the advantages of being able to broadcast outside their national boundaries to other countries, particularly those which are on their borders. Broadcasting can be used to great effect in times of war. The infamous "Lord Haw Haw" of the Second World War is a commonly known example. However there are many more recent examples of broadcasting being used in this way. One of the latest was the events leading up to and during the Gulf War of 1991. During this conflict both sides used some very high power transmitters to reach people on the other side. In addition to this the coalition forces set up stations for their own soldiers to listen to. When any of these stations can be heard they make extremely interesting listening, although it must be accepted that information is highly biassed.

In view of the importance attached to international broadcasting many countries invest huge amounts of money into their transmitters. Accordingly transmitter powers of 100 kW and up are quite common even in some comparatively small countries. This is particularly true in the Gulf region where the cost of power is not a problem in view of the oil reserves they have. In addition to the many high power base stations that are used, many countries have relay stations around the world. For example, the Voice of America broadcasts from many locations around the world. The BBC also has a large number of relays in places including Masirah Island in the Gulf, Ascension Island in the Atlantic and a number of other places as well.

However there are still many low power stations on the air. It is in trying to sort out these stations that much of the skill of a broadcast listener is used. It is often these stations that come from some of the poorer countries in the third world, or alternatively they may only be intended to give comparatively local coverage.

Often listeners will want to collect QSL cards as confirmation that they have heard a particular station. These QSL cards are very similar to those used by radio amateurs, and they are usually very attractive. In order to receive one it is necessary to send off a report to the station in question. Generally the stations require signal reports over a period of a few days together with some details about the programmes being transmitted. In fact many stations mention the information they need in their broadcasts.

Station Identification

Stations have a number of different ways of identifying themselves. Many just use a name. The BBC World Service, the Voice of America (VOA), and Radio Moscow are examples. However, some stations are also issued with callsigns which they generally use along with the station name which usually takes prominence. For example, many stations in the USA will use a callsign beginning with W if it is in the East or K if it is in the West. Another famous station which uses a callsign is HCJB from Ecuador which can often be heard in the 13 metre band. Where callsigns are used they fall into line with the ITU prefix allocations given in the Appendix.

In order to enable listeners to find stations more easily, interval signals (IS) are used. These are short distinctive musical tunes which are played during intervals between programmes especially when the language of the transmission is changing. Generally they will be heard just as the time is coming up to a whole hour, i.e. 1500 hrs. etc. Often these signals will be repeated many times so that they can attract the listener's attention. Other tunes may be longer like the BBC's Lillibulero and they are just played once.

Channels

When scanning these bands it is worth noting that the spacing on the short wave bands is 5 kHz. This is somewhat narrower than that used on the long and medium waves and means that the quality of transmissions is lower. However it has been brought about by the pressure on space caused by the very large number of stations on the air. Transmissions all use AM.

Short Wave Bands

There is a very wide variety of bands open for short wave broadcasts. The broadcast stations make a lot of use of the individual characteristics of each band to enable them to reach the required areas. They usually have a department devoted purely to predicting the best bands to use, however this job is not easy because of the changeable state of the ionosphere. Each transmission will have its particular target area, as the language and programme material have to be chosen to match a particular area. Accordingly the frequency, transmitter aerial, transmitter site and so forth are all chosen to give the best chance of the signal getting through. In addition to this many of the larger stations will use one or more bands either side of the optimum one. This is to try to ensure that even if the propagation conditions on the main band are not ideal then the signal may still be able to get through on a band higher or lower in frequency.

In view of the fact that the state of the ionosphere changes with the seasons and the point in the 11-year sunspot cycle, it is necessary to change the transmission frequency for a particular target area from time to time. Usually this is done at defined intervals in the year so that listeners do not have to follow the station around from one day to the next. Even so this does cause some difficulties. In order to help overcome this problem most stations put out schedules giving times and frequencies as well as their programmes. These schedules can normally be obtained by writing to the station in question and requesting a schedule.

In tropical areas of the world electrical storms create very high levels of interference on the long and medium wave bands. In order to overcome this problem some broadcast bands are allocated to tropical countries within the short wave part of the spectrum. These bands are generally used for domestic broadcasting and are called "tropical bands" for obvious reasons.

Listeners can use the variety of bands to their advantage and by knowing what each band can do the listener can increase his chances of hearing stations from a particular area.

120 Metre Band (2.300 – 2.498 MHz)

This is the lowest in frequency of all the short wave bands. However as it is one of the tropical bands it is not used by stations outside the tropical regions. In general the stations which use this band are low powered and will broadcast in the language of the region. Even so it can still make some interesting listening when conditions are right for stations to be heard.

90 Metre Band (3.200 – 3.400 MHz)

This is another of the tropical bands. Again it is usually used by low powered stations running a kilowatt or so, but there are a few which use higher powers. Generally the best times to use this band are at night during winter months. Signals are not likely to be heard during the day.

75 Metre Band (3.950 – 4.000 MHz)

This band is the lowest frequency non-tropical band but it is only allocated to broadcasters in Region 1. In Region 2 it is allocated to radio amateurs who can often be heard in Europe during the hours of darkness. The band is not particularly popular with either listeners or broadcasters as it is shared with other services and interference levels are high. Even so a number of powerful stations can be heard using it. For example, the BBC have a regular service and other stations like Radio Moscow can be heard as well.

60 Metre Band (4.750 – 5.060 MHz)

This is the highest in frequency of the tropical bands. It has a good variety of stations which can be heard both day and night. There are more powerful stations running many kilo-watts in this band but also there is still a good selection of the lower powered ones. This makes the 60 metre band the most popular of the tropical bands for listeners.

49 Metre Band (5.950 – 6.200 MHz)
This is about the busiest of the short wave broadcast bands. It is packed with high power stations which can be heard both day and night. Despite this it is still possible to hear some low powered stations occasionally but this requires more patience and skill than on some of the other bands.

41 Metre Band (7.100 – 7.300 MHz)
This band is used by a large number of broadcast stations as it offers excellent medium range propagation. Stations can be almost always heard during the day and night, with the night time giving the possibility of hearing longer distance stations. However, in view of the large number of local high powered stations using the band the weaker more distant stations are not always easy to find. In Region 2 this band is allocated to radio amateurs who can sometimes be heard at night between the broadcast stations.

31 Metre Band (9.500 – 9.900 MHz)
This band is quite popular with listeners. Stations can be heard on it for most of the time. During the day stations about 1000 to 2000 km away can be heard. Then particularly at sunrise and sunset it is possible to hear stations much further away. Night time also offers an improvement in conditions.

25 Metre Band (11.650 – 12.050 MHz)
The 25 metre band has many similarities to the 31 metre band. However, being a little higher in frequency it is a little less reliable. Sometimes at night during the winter months no stations may be audible. Even so stations are audible at most times and the band is capable of producing some very long distance signals.

22 Metre Band (13.600 – 13.800 MHz)

This band was allocated to the broadcasting service at the 1979 World Administrative Radio Conference. As such it is comparatively new and may not be marked on all radios. In terms of its performance it has very many similarities with the 25 and 19 metre bands.

19 Metre Band (15.100 – 15.600 MHz)

Being higher in frequency than the 22 metre band this one is more susceptible to the changes in the ionosphere. It is capable of producing stations from all over the world and can prove to be a very interesting band.

16 Metre Band (17.550 – 17.900 MHz)

This is another popular band with short wave broadcast listeners. Like other bands in this section of the spectrum stations may not be audible all of the time, particularly at night, but during the day it is usually possible to hear a good selection of stations. It gives its best performance in periods of high sunspot activity and during the spring and autumn. There is also a better chance of hearing the longer distance stations at dawn and dusk. During the day continental stations are normally audible.

13 Metre Band (21.450 – 21.850 MHz)

This band is capable of producing many long distance stations. It seems to have a higher number of English speaking stations, many of which emanate from North and South America and are beamed at Europe.

11 Metre Band (25.670 – 26.100 MHz)

This is the highest frequency of all the short wave bands. As such it is the least reliable, being very dependent upon the state of the ionosphere. In fact it gives its best performance during periods of high sunspot activity and during the hours of sunlight. When stations are audible they are likely to be quite distant. In view of the unreliability of this band broadcasters are a little reluctant to use it as heavily as the other bands. This means that when the band is open it may not be particularly crowded.

Although broadcasters are allocated distinct bands for their transmissions, the crowded nature of many bands leads a number of broadcasters to transmit outside the normal limits. This means that it is often worth listening either side of the allocated bands to see if there are any other stations which are audible.

VHF and UHF

Whilst there is plenty of activity on the broadcast bands below 30 MHz, the scene in the VHF and UHF portion of the spectrum is growing very fast and offers scanner listeners a vast variety of stations carrying an enormously wide spectrum of programme material. Over the next few years this is bound to increase with the rise in the number of community radio stations which are expected to be introduced.

Within this part of the spectrum there are a number of different broadcast bands. Many are allocated to television although they are not all used in the UK these days as the old 405 line services were closed a number of years ago. A summary of these bands is given in Figure 8.2.

Band	Frequency Range (MHz)	Channel Numbers	Uses
1	41 – 68	1 – 5	405 line TV (these transmissions have now been discontinued in the UK and these bands have been released for other services)
2	87.5 – 108	—	FM Radio
3	174 – 216	6 – 13	405 line TV (see note for band 1)
4	470 – 582	21 – 34	625 line TV
5	614 – 854	39 – 68	625 line TV
6	11700 – 12500	1 – 40	Satellite TV

Fig. 8.2 UK Broadcast Bands above 30 MHz

VHF FM (Sound)

The VHF FM band (Band 2) is generally accepted as the medium for high quality transmissions. This results from the use of FM which can give a better noise performance and in view of the wider bandwidth it can support the better quality associated with these transmissions. In addition to the higher quality a number of other facilities such as stereo and RDS can be supported. Essentially stereo is transmitted by adding a further signal into the transmission. When received by a normal mono receiver it is ignored, but a tuner with a stereo decoder will be able to recover the additional signal and create the two channels of audio required for stereo.

RDS (radio data system) is a comparatively new development mainly intended for car radios. It is a tuning aid which enables receivers with suitable circuitry to identify stations by detecting inaudible digital signals transmitted on the signal. The receiver then decodes the digital information and can then display the name of the station. Using this system the receiver could be made to search for a particular station. When used in a car it could be used to enable the radio to automatically tune from one transmitter to the next as the car moves through the different service areas.

To give the full benefits which FM can offer in terms of higher quality and lower noise the VHF FM signals occupy a much wider bandwidth than other sound broadcast signals. They have a maximum frequency deviation of ±75 kHz and a total bandwidth of 200 kHz. To receive these stations the scanner should be set to wideband FM or WFM. Channels are spaced every 100 kHz although the frequency planning normally means that in any one location stations which can be heard are normally more than 100 kHz apart.

With more national and local services being implemented a band plan has been devised. This will enable listeners to be able to tune to the correct portion of the band depending upon what they want to listen to.

With the number of national and local radio stations active around the country, there is plenty for the scanner listener to pick up from both near and far. With a reasonably sited aerial it is surprising how many different stations can be picked up. In addition to these stations a large number of

Frequency (MHz)	Service
87.5 – 88.0	Not allocated
88.0 – 90.2	Radio 2
90.2 – 92.4	Radio 3
92.4 – 94.6	Radio 4
94.6 – 96.1	BBC Local Radio
96.1 – 97.6	Independent Local Radio
97.6 – 99.8	Radio 1
99.8 – 102.0	Independent National Radio
102.0 – 103.5	Independent Local Radio
103.5 – 105.0	BBC Local Radio
105.0 – 108.0	Community Radio

Fig. 8.3 UK VHF FM Broadcast Band Plan

community stations are being set up, but as they operate on much lower power levels they are not as likely to be heard over such great distances.

Television
Television is another broadcast service which can be heard above in the VHF and UHF sections of the frequency spectrum. Although there are allocations for television broadcasts between 41 and 68 MHz and 174 and 216 MHz these allocations are no longer used in the UK as they were used to carry the old 405 line transmissions which have now been discontinued. However, some countries still use these frequencies and when there is a lift in propagation conditions either as a result of tropospheric ducting or sporadic E these stations can be heard.

The terrestrial television transmissions in the UK are broadcast in the UHF portion of the spectrum. Whilst the video signal cannot be deciphered on a scanner it is possible to listen to the audio signal. Each channel has its own distinct frequencies for the sound and vision signals as shown in Figure 8.4.

Channel Number	Vision Carrier Frequency	Sound Carrier Frequency
21	471.25	477.25
22	479.25	485.25
23	487.25	493.25
24	495.25	501.25
25	503.25	509.25
26	511.25	517.25
27	519.25	525.25
28	527.25	533.25
29	535.25	541.25
30	543.25	549.25
31	551.25	557.25
32	559.25	565.25
33	567.25	573.25
34	575.25	581.25
39	615.25	621.25
40	623.25	629.25
41	631.25	637.25
42	639.25	645.25
43	647.25	653.25
44	655.25	661.25
45	663.25	669.25
46	671.25	677.25
47	679.25	685.25
48	687.25	693.25
49	695.25	701.25
50	703.25	709.25
51	711.25	717.25
52	719.25	725.25
53	727.25	733.25
54	735.25	741.25
55	743.25	749.25
56	751.25	757.25
57	759.25	765.25
58	767.25	773.25
59	775.25	781.25
60	783.25	789.25
61	791.25	797.25
62	799.25	805.25
63	807.25	813.25
64	815.25	821.25
65	823.25	829.25
66	831.25	837.25
67	839.25	845.25
68	847.25	853.25

All frequencies are in MHz

Fig. 8.4 UK UHF Television Channel Frequencies

Chapter 9

AMATEUR RADIO

At various points in the spectrum it is possible to hear radio amateurs or "hams" talking to one another. Unlike most of the other users of the radio spectrum radio amateurs are using their radios as a hobby, and not for some commercial use.

What is Amateur Radio?

Amateur radio is a hobby which grew up with radio itself. Way back in the earliest days of radio there were people who wanted to be able to transmit their own signals and experiment with transmitters.

Today amateur radio is a thriving hobby. It has many aspects to interest a wide variety of people. Some people will enjoy the excitement of contacting people around the world. Others will enjoy chatting to friends around town. There is also a very strong contingent of hams who construct their own equipment, and come on the air with transmitters they built themselves. Many people enjoy generally experimenting and finding out more about radio, and in fact this has contributed greatly to our knowledge of topics like radio propagation. Amateur radio has also been taken into space. There are a number of amateur satellites in orbit which can be accessed on a number of bands. In addition to this amateurs have actually operated from space. There have been a number of amateurs who have been up in the Shuttle and operated from there, and also the first British astronaut, Helen Sharman, operated from space when she went up with the Russians. All of these aspects are part of amateur radio which forms an interesting hobby on its own.

Whilst anyone can listen to radio amateurs it is necessary to obtain a licence before any transmissions can be made. In most countries a theory examination will have to be passed before a licence to transmit on frequencies above 30 MHz will be granted. Before a licence covering all the amateur bands will be issued a morse test generally has to be passed. In order to find out more about the conditions it is best to apply to the national radio society of your particular country. In the United Kingdom it is the Radio Society of Great Britain, Lambda House, Cranborne Road, Potters Bar, Hertfordshire EN6 3JE.

Jargon

In common with other aspects of radio operating there is specialised jargon and a number of abbreviations associated more closely with this hobby and not found very much elsewhere. Many of these abbreviations date back to the first days of radio or even earlier to the days of the old telegraph systems when morse was the only means of sending information. Many of these abbreviations have remained and are incorporated into the "ham" vocabulary.

CQ	A general call asking for a contact
CW	Continuous wave (used to denote a morse signal)
BCI	Broadcast receiver interference
DX	Long Distance
FB	Fine Business
HI	Laughter
Mod	Modulation
PA	Power Amplifier
SWL	Short Wave Listener
TVI	Television Interference
WX	Weather
XTAL	Crystal
XYL	Wife
YL	Young Lady
73	Best Regards
88	Love and Kisses

Fig. 9.1 Amateur Radio Jargon

Apart from these abbreviations the Q Code outlined in Chapter 7 is widely used. In addition to this a system of reporting signal strengths is used. It is very useful because it

Readability

R1	Unreadable
R2	Barely readable
R3	Readable with difficulty
R4	Readable with little difficulty
R5	Perfectly readable

Strength

S1	Barely detectable
S2	Very weak signals
S3	Weak signals
S4	Fair signals
S5	Fairly good signals
S6	Good signals
S7	Moderately strong signals
S8	Strong signals
S9	Very strong signals

Tone

T1	Extremely rough note
T2	Very rough note
T3	Rough note
T4	Fairly rough note
T5	Note modulated with strong ripple
T6	Modulated note
T7	Near DC note but with smooth ripple
T8	Near DC note but with trace of ripple
T9	Pure DC note

Fig. 9.2 RST Code for Readability, Strength and Tone

helps to give a standard by which different reports can be compared. The basic system is shown in Figure 9.2. It consists of a number for the readability, the strength, and the tone. When using speech the last number for the tone is omitted as this is only used for morse.

Callsigns

Listening on the amateur bands it is quite possible to hear stations from many different countries. Each station is given its own callsign. One example is the callsign G3YWX. From this it can be seen that it can be broken up into two parts. The first is the prefix which includes the characters up to and including the last number. In this case it is G3. By comparing the prefix with the list in Appendix III then the country of the station can be identified. In this case it is England. Another callsign might be VP8ANT. This station was in fact located in Antarctica.

The second part of the callsign is purely a serial number so that the particular station can be identified.

Occasionally amateur radio operators will want to operate abroad. Sometimes a completely new callsign will be allocated. However, in some instances the station will keep his own callsign but place the prefix of the new country in front of his home call. For example F/G3YWX would be operating in France. Sometimes a previous system is used whereby the prefix of the country being visited is placed after the callsign, e.g. G3YWX/VP9.

Frequency Allocations

Amateur radio enthusiasts are allocated a wide selection of bands throughout the radio spectrum. This means that virtually all scanners should cover at least one and it is more than likely that several more will be covered depending upon the coverage of the scanner (see Figure 9.3).

Modes

Amateur licences permit a wide variety of types of transmission to be made. Amplitude modulation is used very little. Single sideband is the favourite mode for long distance voice communications on both the HF and VHF/UHF bands. Frequency modulation is widely used for local and mobile contacts in the VHF portion of the spectrum and above. It is particularly useful because the signal strength variations caused by the movement of a mobile station can be all but removed in the receiver.

Frequency Limits (MHz)		Approximate Wavelength
1.81	2.0	160 Metres (Top Band)
3.50	3.80	80 Metres
7.00	7.10	40 Metres
10.10	10.15	30 Metres
14.00	14.35	20 Metres
18.068	18.168	17 Metres
21.00	21.45	15 Metres
24.89	24.99	12 Metres
28.00	29.70	10 Metres
50.00	52.00	6 Metres
70.00	70.50	4 Metres
144.00	146.00	2 Metres
430.00	440.00	70 cms
1240.00	1325.00	23 cms
2310.00	2450.00	13 cms
3400.00	3475.00	9 cms
5650.00	5680.00	
5755.00	5765.00	} 6 cms
5820.00	5850.00	
10000	10500	3 cms
24000	24250	
47000	47200	
75500	76000	
142000	144000	
248000	250000	

Fig. 9.3 UK Amateur Bands

Morse still finds a lot of use. A large number of the contacts on the HF bands use it although its use above 30 MHz is still quite limited.

Repeaters

Many radio amateurs operate equipment from their cars. In fact mobile operation is particularly popular in the VHF and UHF bands because at these frequencies reasonably efficient aerials can be made. However, one of the major problems is that range is limited because the location may be poor. Lack of height combined with the screening effect of nearby buildings can mean that signals from mobile stations are weak. To help overcome this problem a network of repeaters has been set up.

Essentially a repeater is just a unit which receives on one frequency and transmits on another. As the repeater will be located on a good site it will have a good coverage of the surrounding area and it will be able to pick up stations with weak signals. Once the signal from the station has been relayed it will be able to be heard over the whole coverage area of the repeater. This will enable stations to have contacts through the repeater where they would otherwise not be able to hear one another as shown in Figure 9.4.

As the repeater will have to transmit and receive at the same time, it needs to receive and transmit on two different frequencies. The frequency on which it listens or receives is called the input channel, whereas the frequency on which it transmits is called the output channel. The difference in frequency must be sufficient for the receiver not to be unduly affected by the transmitter. Normally on the 2 metre band the difference is 600 kHz and on 70 cms the difference is 1.6 MHz.

When listening to a repeater a number of different tones will be heard. When there are no signals on the input channel to be relayed the repeater will be dormant, but even so it will turn itself on periodically to transmit its callsign in morse. This appears as an audio tone modulated onto the carrier.

In order to operate the repeater the transmitting station will need to transmit a short tone or tone burst. This normally lasts for about half a second and is at a frequency of about 1750 Hz. The idea of this tone is to prevent spurious signals and noise from opening up the repeater.

When stations are in contact they will not need to transmit their tone burst again. However a few other tones may be heard. When stations pass transmission from one to another it is necessary to leave a small break. When this happens the repeater will transmit a "k" in morse as an invitation for the other station to start transmitting. At the same time the

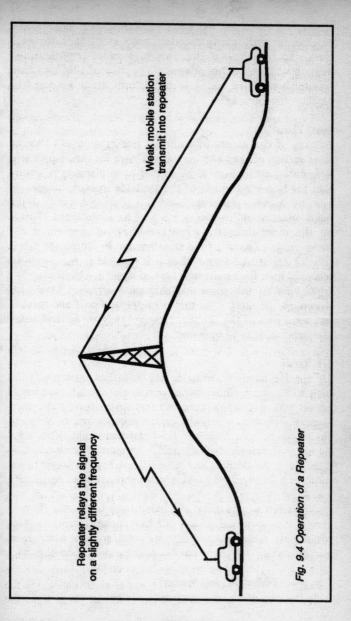

Weak mobile station transmit into repeater

Repeater relays the signal on a slightly different frequency

Fig. 9.4 Operation of a Repeater

timers in the repeater will be reset. The timer is included in a repeater to only allow a certain amount of time for each station to transmit. If this time is exceeded then the transmission will stop being relayed. The idea of this is to limit transmission times and prevent stations from keeping the repeater for too long.

Band Plans

In view of the variety of modes of transmission and also the wide variety of uses which amateurs have for their equipment it is necessary to have some sort of band planning to ensure that the best use is made of the available spectrum space. In fact by keeping different modes in different parts of the band unnecessary interference is kept to a minimum. This is all the more necessary when consideration is given to the heavy usage of some of the same bands. In addition to this it is a lot easier to operate when it is possible to narrow down where to look for a particular type of signal in a band.

In view of this some international band plans have been drawn up. In most cases they are not mandatory and they do not form part of the licence. However they are adhered to by the great majority of operators.

HF Bands

On the HF bands planning is less rigid than on some of the higher frequency bands. Whilst portions of the different bands are set aside for different modes there are no distinct channels. Generally stations will find a clear frequency and use it. Even so it will be seen from the HF band plans that there are a number of frequencies set aside for particular uses. One example is the QRP or low power frequency. However this is more of a frequency around which people tend to congregate (see Figure 9.5).

There is a wide variety of bands to use within the HF portion of the spectrum. Each one has its own character. This means that each band will have its own particular advantages, and by using different bands the best results can be obtained.

1.810 – 2.000 MHz (160 Metres)

This is the lowest frequency amateur band and it is shared

1.810	–	1.840	CW
1.840	–	2.000	Phone and CW
3.500	–	3.600	CW
3.500	–	3.510	Intercontinental Contacts
3.560			QRP Frequency
3.600	–	3.800	Phone and CW
7.000	–	7.040	CW
7.030			QRP Frequency
7.040	–	7.100	Phone and CW
10.100	–	10.140	CW
10.106			QRP Frequency
10.140	–	10.150	CW and RTTY
14.000	–	14.099	CW
14.060			QRP Frequency
14.099	–	14.101	Beacons
14.101	–	14.350	Phone and CW
18.068	–	18.100	CW
18.100	–	18.110	CW and RTTY
18.110	–	18.168	Phone and CW
21.000	–	21.149	CW Only
21.060			QRP Frequency
21.149	–	21.151	Beacons
21.151	–	21.450	Phone and CW
24.890	–	24.920	CW
24.920	–	24.930	CW and RTTY
24.930	–	24.990	Phone and CW
28.000	–	28.190	CW Only
28.060			QRP Frequency
28.190	–	28.225	Beacons
28.225	–	29.700	Phone and CW

Fig. 9.5 HF Band Plan

with other services. It is not widely used, but it can be very interesting to scan from time to time. Under day time conditions local signals up to 30 miles or a little more are audible. However at night time signals which are further afield can be heard. During the winter months it is not uncommon for transatlantic contacts to be made, and on occasions contacts can be made to the other side of the globe. If one is to hear even the transatlantic contacts a good aerial will be needed.

3.500 – 3.800 MHz (80 Metres)
This band is also shared but it is used considerably more than 160 metres. It provides a good band for contacts within the country, and then at night signals more distant can be heard very easily. Transatlantic contacts are fairly common, but it should be remembered that Region 2 has its allocation extended up to 4.00 MHz and some SSB signals will be heard in the section above 3.8 MHz. The main disadvantage of 80 metres is that it becomes very noisy at night when signals from further afield are heard. Amateur stations have to find clear frequencies between the commercial users.

7.000 – 7.100 MHz (40 Metres)
The forty metre band is allocated only to the amateur service but it is normally quite crowded because the bandwidth is quite small. Under daytime conditions stations up to a few hundred miles distance can be heard. Then as night falls more distant stations can be heard.

10.100 – 10.150 MHz (30 Metres)
In 1979 a number of new bands were allocated to amateurs at the World Administrative Radio Conference (WARC). The 30 metre band was the lowest in frequency. It is not very wide and is still used by a number of other services. As a result CW is only used on it at present, but even so for those who can read morse it does provide some interesting stations.

14.000 – 14.350 MHz (20 Metres)
This is the major long distance or DX band. It is generally possible to hear stations from all over Europe during the day. In the early morning stations from the other side of the

globe are generally plentiful and then in the evening transatlantic stations can be heard from both North and South America. Often stations can be heard at night although this is quite dependent upon the season and time in the sunspot cycle.

18.068 – 18.168 MHz (17 Metres)
This band was only released for use by radio amateurs after the World Administrative Radio Conference in 1979. Even then countries took some time to allow amateurs to use it. Accordingly it is not as well used as some of the more established bands. Despite this it can provide some interesting stations, and in terms of propagation it has many similarities with both 20 metres and 15 metres.

21.000 – 21.450 MHz (15 Metres)
Like 20 metres this is another popular band. Being higher in frequency its conditions are more variable although it will be possible to hear long distance stations for a large proportion of time.

24.890 – 24.990 (12 Metres)
Like the 17 metre band, 12 metres was released after 1979. It provides some interesting long haul stations but is very dependent upon the state of the ionosphere like 10 metres but it does stay open for longer as it is slightly lower in frequency.

28.000 – 29.700 MHz (10 Metres)
This band is the highest in frequency of the HF bands. It is also the one which has the widest bandwidth. This means that it can be used for a larger number of modes than some of the narrower bands. Morse is used up to 28.190 MHz and SSB is used below 29.0 MHz. Above this frequency FM is becoming popular, and there are a number of repeaters on these frequencies. Some of them in the U.S.A. relay signals onto 2 metres so that crossband contacts can take place.

Being the highest frequency HF band it is most dependent upon the state of the ionosphere. At periods around the sunspot maxima it is possible to hear stations from all over the world during the day. However, during the sunspot minima there is propagation via the ionosphere and is often limited to sporadic E.

VHF and UHF Bands

Band plans on the VHF and UHF bands are a little more wide ranging than on the HF bands. The extra bandwidth coupled with the additional modes which are used make this necessary.

In addition to the basic band plans outlining where the different modes should be used, the widespread use of FM has resulted in channels being used for this mode. These channels have a spacing of 25 kHz. This allows sufficient bandwidth for a strong signal on one channel not to interfere with stations on the adjacent channels. However with the pressure on space there is some talk of reducing the channel spacing to 12.5 kHz.

Each channel is designated a number for easy identification. On 2 metres the simplex channels start with the letter S followed by a number for each individual channel. Then on 70 cms the simplex channel numbers start with SU. To give an example of how they are used, a simplex channel on 2 metres could be S20 whereas one on 70 cms would be SU20.

Repeater channels are given similar designations but they start with the letter R on 2 metres and RB on 70 cms. However, for repeater channels there will be an input and output channel which have to be defined in each instance.

A system of calling channels has also been instigated for non-repeater operation. As the name suggests the channels or frequencies are used only to make initial calls. Once a contact has been established then the stations should move off the calling channel to another one. This will then leave the calling frequency or channel free for others. This idea has become very useful. In view of the comparatively wide bandwidths which are available it enables people to monitor a single frequency to hear CQ calls or people calling specific stations to see if they are listening.

Like the HF bands the VHF and UHF bands also have their own distinctive characteristics. In order to make the best use of them it is necessary to know a little about each band.

6 Metres

This band has only been released to amateurs in the UK since the old 405 line transmissions finished. Whilst it is used by many other countries around the world, including the USA, it is by no means a band in general use. Even so it is being released to more European countries now that television services are being moved to the UHF portion of the spectrum.

In the United Kingdom the band only cover 50.0 to 52.0 MHz whilst the band plan for Region 1 identifies frequencies up to 54.0 MHz. The reason for this is that the allocation extends this far in some countries. When devising the plan this was taken into account and no modes are excluded for those without the full allocation.

Frequencies (MHz)	Modes allowed or use
50.0 – 50.02	CW only
50.02 – 50.08	CW and Beacons
50.08 – 50.10	CW only
50.10 – 51.00	Narrow band modes (CW, SSB, AM, RTTY, SSTV)
50.20	SSB calling frequency
50.60	RTTY calling frequency
51.00 – 51.10	Pacific DX Window
51.10 – 52.00	All modes including FM and repeaters
52.00 – 52.10	Pacific DX Window, narrow band only
52.10 – 54.0	All modes including FM and repeaters

Fig. 9.6 Region 1 Band Plan for 6 Metres

4 Metres

This band is allocated in only very few countries. This means that there is very little commercial equipment available for it. As a result most people build their own equipment or modify ex-PMR transceivers. Even so activity is fairly low in comparison with some other bands.

Frequency (MHz)	Modes allowed or use
70.000 – 70.075	Beacons
70.075 – 70.150	CW
70.150 – 70.260	SSB
70.200	SSB calling frequency
70.260 – 70.400	All modes
70.260	Mobile calling frequency
70.300	RTTY calling frequency
70.400 – 70.500	FM
70.450	FM calling frequency

Fig. 9.7 UK Band Plan for 4 Metres

2 Metres

This is the most popular of all the VHF and UHF bands. This has come about for many reasons. One is obviously the availability of equipment, and another is the manageable size of the aerials. Other reasons are historical. For a long time 2 metres was the lowest frequency band which could be used by class B licensees in the UK, and as lower frequency equipment is usually easier to build and cheaper to buy this made 2 metres very attractive.

Two metres is used for a wide cross section of interests. However there are broadly three main sections, namely: FM, the DX modes including SSB and CW, and finally data transmission. The FM portion of the band occupying most of the band above 145 MHz is very heavily used in view of the popularity of FM. There is also a wide network of repeaters which means that there is repeater coverage over much of the country.

Operation using the "DX" modes takes place in the lower quarter of the band as shown in Figure 9.8. Although there is some CW operation the vast majority of operation is on SSB.

Frequency (MHz)	Modes allowed or use
144.000 − 144.150	CW only
144.000 − 144.025	Moonbounce operation
144.050	CW calling frequency
144.100	Meteor scatter (CW)
144.150 − 144.500	SSB and CW
144.300	SSB calling frequency
144.400	Meteor scatter (SSB)
144.500 − 144.850	All modes
144.500	Slow scan TV
144.600	RTTY
144.625	Packet radio
144.650	Mailboxes
144.675	Packet radio
144.700	Fax calling frequency
144.750	TV calling and talkback frequency
144.845 − 144.990	Beacons
145.000 − 145.800	FM simplex and repeaters
145.800 − 146.000	Satellite operation

Fig. 9.8 Band Plan for 2 Metres

Although the more serious DX operation takes place in this section of the band, it is often used for local contacts as well.

In view of the large increase in popularity of the data modes of transmission there is a lot of activity in this area as well. Packet radio is particularly popular and there is a growing network of mailboxes around the country.

For 2 metre channel designations − see Figure 9.9.

Frequency (MHz)	Channel Designation	
145.00	R0	Repeater Input Channels
145.025	R1	
145.050	R2	
145.075	R3	
145.100	R4	
145.125	R5	
145.150	R6	
145.175	R7	
145.200	S8	Simplex Channels
145.225	S9	
145.250	S10	
145.275	S11	
145.300	S12	
145.325	S13	
145.350	S14	
145.375	S15	
145.400	S16	
145.425	S17	
145.450	S18	
145.475	S19	
145.500	S20	
145.525	S21	
145.550	S22	
145.575	S23	
145.600	R0	Repeater Output Channels
145.625	R1	
145.650	R2	
145.675	R3	
145.700	R4	
145.725	R5	
145.750	R6	
145.775	R7	

Fig. 9.9 2 Metre Channel Designations

116

70 Centimetres

Next to 2 metres, 70 cms is probably the next most popular of the VHF/UHF bands. Often people will move up to this band when 2 metres becomes crowded, and it has many similarities to its lower frequency counterpart. Also there is plenty of commercial equipment available for the band. In addition to this there are ex-PMR units which can be bought quite cheaply and easily modified. However, as it has a much wider bandwidth it can support activities like amateur television which require a large amount of space.

It is quite likely that 70 cms will be used increasingly in the future as the new novice licensees are given an allocation between 433.0 and 435.0 MHz.

Although this band plan is correct for the UK there are a few differences which will be encountered in other countries.

Frequency (MHz)	Modes allowed or use
432.000 – 432.150	CW only
432.000 – 432.025	Moonbounce
432.050	Centre of CW activity
432.150 – 432.500	SSB and CW
432.200	Centre of SSB activity
432.350	Microwave talkback
432.500 – 432.800	All modes
432.500	Centre of slow scan TV activity
432.600	Centre of RTTY activity
432.625	Packet radio links
432.650	Packet radio links
432.675	Packet radio
432.700	Centre of fax activity
432.800 – 433.000	Beacons
433.000 – 433.375	Output for 1.6 MHz shift repeaters
433.400 – 434.600	FM simplex
433.625	Packet radio
433.650	Packet radio

Fig. 9.10 Band Plan for 70 cms

Frequency (MHz)	Modes allowed or use
433.675	Packet radio
434.600 – 435.000	Input for 1.6 MHz shift repeaters
435.000 – 438.000	Satellite operation
434.000 – 440.000	TV operation

Fig. 9.10 Continued

Frequency (MHz)	Channel Designation	
433.000	RB0	Repeater Channels
433.025	RB1	
433.050	RB2	
433.075	RB3	
433.100	RB4	
433.125	RB5	
433.150	RB6	
433.175	RB7	
433.200	RB8	
433.225	RB9	
433.250	RB10	
433.275	RB11	
433.300	RB12	
433.325	RB13	
433.350	RB14	
433.375	RB15	
433.400	SU16	Simplex Channels
433.425	SU17	
433.450	SU18	
433.475	SU19	
433.500	SU20	
433.525	SU21	

Fig. 9.11 70 cms Channel Designations

Frequency (MHz)	Channel Designation	
433.550	SU22	
433.575	SU23	
433.600	SU24	
434.600	RB0	Repeater Channels
434.625	RB1	
434.650	RB2	
434.675	RB3	
434.700	RB4	
434.725	RB5	
434.750	RB6	
434.775	RB7	
434.800	RB8	
434.825	RB9	
434.850	RB10	
434.875	RB11	
434.900	RB12	
434.925	RB13	
434.950	RB14	
434.975	RB15	

Fig. 9.11 Continued

Locators

One feature of VHF and UHF operation is the practice of using what is called the QRA locator system. Essentially it is a system which has been devised to enable stations to give their locations fairly accurately without having to resort to the latitude and longitude.

The system which is in general use today is called the Maidenhead System and it is approved by the International Amateur Radio Union (IARU). It splits the world up into a matrix of main squares which occupy 10 degrees latitude by 20 degree longitude. These squares are designated by two letters. The first refers to the longitude and the second to

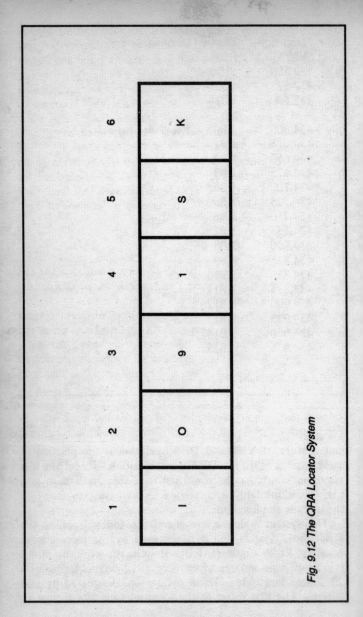

Fig. 9.12 The QRA Locator System

the latitude. They start at 180 degrees west and 90 degrees south with the square AA and finish at 180 degrees east and 90 degrees north with RR. They are letters 1 and 2 in Figure 9.12.

These squares are each subdivided into a hundred smaller squares occupying 2 degrees of longitude and 1 degree of latitude. These squares are given numeric designations starting with 00 in the south west and 99 in the north east. These two numbers occupy positions 3 and 4 in the locator.

A final subdivision is made to enable the location to be fixed even more precisely. These areas are designated by letters starting with AA and finishing with XX and they occupy the last two positions in the locator. The size of these last areas is 5' longitude by 2.5' latitude.

QSL Cards

Listening on the amateur bands and in particular on the HF bands, many stations will be heard to talk about QSL cards. The name is derived from the Q code and means to confirm receipt. QSL cards are used to confirm contacts between stations. Normally they are postcard sized and contain all the relevant information about the contact including the date, time, frequency and mode used and so forth. In addition to this they will obviously contain the callsign of the station as well as the location. A typical card is shown in Figure 9.13. However, some cards are particularly colourful and may even have a photograph of the locality or the station itself. In fact collecting these cards almost becomes an interest in itself.

Contests

One aspect of amateur radio which appeals to many people is that of participating in a contest. A number of contests are arranged throughout the year on different bands. The rules will obviously change from one contest to the next but it gives the scanner user the opportunity to hear stations from locations which might not normally be on the air.

Contests generally have a fixed weekend during the year when they take place. These dates have been evolved over the years so that events can be spread out in a sensible fashion

G3YWX

OPERATOR: IAN POOLE

TO RADIO ———— CONFIRMING AM/CW SSB QSO OF ————

AT ———— G.M.T. FREQ. ———— MHz YOUR SIGS RST ————

TX: ———— INPUT ———— WATTS

RX: ———— ANTENNA: ————

REMARKS ————

PSE / TKS QSL DIRECT / VIA RSGB ———— 73 de ————

Fig. 9.13 A typical QSL card

122

so that they do not clash. A summary of the major events during the year is set out in Figure 9.14.

Contest	Bands	Date	Comments
ARRL DX Contest (CW)	HF	Third Full W/E February	Stations contact USA/Canada
ARRL DX Contest (SSB)	HF	First Full W/E March	Stations contact USA/Canada
CQ-Worked PrefiXes (WPX) (SSB)	HF	Last Full W/E March	Stations contact as many stations as possible. Extra points given for new prefixes contacted.
CQ-Worked PrefiXes (WPX) (CW)	HF	Last Full W/E May	Stations contact as many other stations as possible. Extra points given for new prefixes which are contacted.
CW Field Day (UK) (CW)	HF	Usually 1st W/E June	British portable stations make as many contacts as possible.
All Asia (SSB)	HF	Third Full W/E June	Contact stations in Asia.
VHF Field Day (SSB/CW)	VHF	First Full W/E July	British portable stations make as many contacts as possible. Operation is mainly SSB.
IARU-Radiosport (SSB/CW)	HF	Second Full W/E July	Contact as many stations as possible. Extra points given for new countries contacted.
Worked All Europe-DX (CW)	HF	Second Full W/E August	Stations outside Europe contact as many European stations as possible.
All Asia (CW)	HF	Last Full W/E August	Contact stations in Asia.
SSB Field Day (SSB)	HF	First Full W/E September	Portable stations make as many contacts as possible.
RSGB Trophy	VHF	First Full W/E September	Many portable stations set up. Aim of contest is to make as many contacts as possible.
Worked All Europe-DX (SSB)	HF	Second Full W/E September	Stations outside Europe to contact as many European stations as possible.
CQ-WorldWide (SSB)	HF	Last Full W/E October	Contact as many stations in as many countries as possible.
CQ-WorldWide (CW)	HF	Last Full W/E November	Contact as many stations in as many countries as possible.

124

Chapter 10

CITIZEN'S BAND

The idea for a band which could be used by any citizen initially came from the USA. Unlike amateur licences a knowledge of radio theory or the morse code was not needed allowing people to simply pay for the licence and then go on the air. Obviously restrictions had to be imposed. Equipment had to be approved and powers were limited to 5 watts maximum.

The idea was very successful and a large number of these citizens' bands or CB licences were issued. In fact so many people used it that the band was always crowded and there was a lot of interference.

With their introduction people were able to use it for a large number of purposes. Some just wanted to talk over the air. Others used it for short range portable communications. Truckers were one major group of users. They used to use it to chat to one another on their long journeys and the CB became a companion in the cab. It also served as a means of warning about traffic congestion and road conditions. Along with the rise in popularity of CB came a new and colourful set of jargon.

One interest which sprang up was that of making long distance contacts. Although it is illegal in the USA to make contacts with stations over 150 miles away, this rule was difficult to enforce and many people disregard it. Normally contacts can only be made over distances of up to 25 miles or so, and even this is not easy when interference levels are high. However, when the right propagation conditions exist it is possible to make contacts with stations several thousand miles away. It is even possible for stations in the USA to be heard in the UK on occasions.

Once CB was established in the USA the idea quickly spread to many other countries around the globe. To give a measure of its success most of the Communist Bloc Eastern European countries had introduced it by the late 1970s. However at this time there was no allocation in the UK.

CB in the UK

In view of the popularity of CB around the globe, and the number of sets being manufactured, it was not surprising that some started to find their way into Britain. Around the late 1970s the number of sets entering the country rapidly increased and illegal CB activity rose dramatically. As the American Citizens' Band used the same frequencies that were allocated to radio control in Britain, model makers were forced to stop using these frequencies and were allocated another band slightly higher in frequency.

Finally CB was legally introduced in the UK in November 1981. However, unlike the USA where AM and SSB were used, FM was the mode which had to be used. This possessed a number of advantages. The main one was that FM was likely to cause less interference to television and hi-fi sets than AM or SSB. The power was also kept quite low at 4 watts and there were restrictions placed on aerials. On the positive side two bands were introduced. One was on the popular 27 MHz portion of the spectrum whilst a second was at 934 MHz.

The channels for the original 27 MHz band were different to those used elsewhere and they are shown in Figure 101. The distances which can be achieved on this band in the UK are the same as in the USA. However to achieve them a good aerial is needed. Unfortunately discones and other receiving aerials do not perform very well because they are generally at the bottom of their operating range or even below it. As a result they will be inefficient and they also have a much higher angle of radiation. For the best results a good CB aerial is needed with a low angle of radiation or reception.

In order to bring the UK into line with the rest of Europe a new set of channels is now available for use. These "CEPT" frequencies are given in Figure 10.2. These new channels are the same as those used in the rest of Europe as well as the USA. In view of this it is quite possible that AM or SSB may be heard on them from time to time. Although it is possible these signals could emanate from the States it is far more likely that they have come from someone using an illegal CB set in this country.

Channel	Frequency	Channel	Frequency
1	27.60125	21	27.80125
2	27.61125	22	27.81125
3	27.62125	23	27.82125
4	27.63125	24	27.83125
5	27.64125	25	27.84125
6	27.65125	26	27.85125
7	27.66125	27	27.86125
8	27.67125	28	27.87125
9	27.68125	29	27.88125
10	27.69125	30	27.89125
11	27.70125	31	27.90125
12	27.71125	32	27.91125
13	27.72125	33	27.92125
14	27.73125	34	27.93125
15	27.74125	35	27.94125
16	27.75125	36	27.95125
17	27.76125	37	27.96125
18	27.77125	38	27.97125
19	27.78125	39	27.98125
20	27.79125	40	27.99125

Fig. 10.1 27 MHz Band – MPT1320 (27/81)

The two systems are currently both in use, although rigs are only available with one set of channels or the other and not both. In view of the fact that the new CEPT channels are more widely used the older UK only ones are likely to fall into disuse over the years.

The 27 MHz band is by far the most popular. Equipment is cheap and relatively easy to instal. The 934 MHz or UHF band is used far less because equipment is much more expensive and requires more expertise during installation. As a result most of the users of this band are small businesses.

Unlike the 27 MHz the UHF band has only 20 channels as shown in Figure 10.3. Distances which can be reached are

Channel	Frequency	Channel	Frequency
1	26.965	21	27.215
2	26.975	22	27.225
3	26.985	23	27.255
4	27.005	24	27.235
5	27.015	25	27.245
6	27.025	26	27.265
7	27.035	27	27.275
8	27.055	28	27.285
9	27.065	29	27.295
10	27.075	30	27.305
11	27.085	31	27.315
12	27.105	32	27.325
13	27.115	33	27.335
14	27.125	34	27.345
15	27.135	35	27.355
16	27.155	36	27.365
17	27.165	37	27.375
18	27.175	38	27.385
19	27.185	39	27.395
20	27.205	40	27.405

Fig. 10.2 27 MHz Band – MPT1333 (PR 27/GB) CEPT

Channel	Frequency	Channel	Frequency
1	934.025	11	934.525
2	934.075	12	934.575
3	934.125	13	934.625
4	934.175	14	934.675
5	934.225	15	934.725
6	934.275	16	934.775
7	934.325	17	934.825
8	934.375	18	934.875
9	934.425	19	934.925
10	934.475	20	934.975

Fig. 10.3 934 MHz Band – MPT1321 (934/81)

often less than on 27 MHz. Usually they are around five to ten miles although with a tropospheric lift much greater distances are possible.

Procedure

The procedure for operating a CB station is far less rigorous than it is for other services like amateur radio, ship-to-shore and the like. Even so there are some codes of practice which are adhered to.

Many hobbyists adopt a handle as a means of identification. In many cases it will reflect something about the person, and it is very useful because it identifies the person better than a first name which may be shared by several people in the same area.

In addition to handles there is a certain amount of jargon associated with CB. Much of it has come over from the States but in line with the recommendations in the CB licence comparatively little is used in the UK. Probably the most famous code for CB is the "10" code which is used by police and emergency services in the USA as well as CB operators. There are codes from 10-1 (pronounced ten one) to 10-99, and some of the more common ones are listed in Figure 10.4.

10-1	Unable to copy, change location
10-2	Signal good
10-3	Stop transmitting
10-4	OK
10-9	Repeat
10-12	Stand-by
10-20	Location
10-33	Emergency
10-50	Accident
10-74	Negative
10-97	Check signal

Fig. 10.4 Commonly Used "Ten" Codes

Although nobody has the right to any channels, certain ones are allotted for special purposes and should be kept for them if at all possible. Channel 9 is used as an emergency channel and should be kept clear unless it is really needed. Channel 14 is a calling channel. Stations can use it for calling other stations to see if they are available in much the same way amateur stations use calling channels on their VHF and UHF bands. Once contact has been established they should move off and leave it clear for others. In this way people only have to monitor one channel for calls. Channel 19 is designated a mobile channel.

Finally the CB licence states that a CB licence is required even to receive CB transmissions.

Appendix I

GLOSSARY OF TERMINOLOGY

Active Aerial: A receiving aerial which includes an amplifier as part of the design. By doing this its size can be made much smaller.

Aerial: The wire or other item which picks up or radiates radio signals.

A.F.: Audio frequency — frequencies in the audio spectrum. Normally this is taken to be between about 20 Hz and 20 kHz.

A.M.: Amplitude modulation. This is a form of modulation of a radio signal where its amplitude or strength is varied in line with the sound. A.M. is used by broadcast stations on the Long, Medium and Short Wave bands.

AMTOR: This stands for Amateur Telex Over Radio. It is a form of data communication devised for amateurs and will operate under conditions with interference and fading.

Antenna: An aerial.

Bandwidth: The width or amount of spectrum space that a signal occupies. An A.M. signal will generally take up about 6 kHz whilst a CW or morse one will only occupy a few Hz.

Baud: A unit used to describe the rate at which data is transferred. One baud is equal to one "bit" per second.

Beam: An aerial which is directive and can beam or concentrate more power in one direction than another when it is transmitting. Alternatively when receiving it is more "sensitive" in one direction than the others.

Beat Frequency Oscillator (B.F.O.): An oscillator used in a receiver to create a beat note with incoming signals, e.g. morse

131

and make them audible. A B.F.O. is also used for the reception of single sideband.

Burner: A CB term for a power amplifier used to boost the power of a transmitter.

Carrier Insertion Oscillator (C.I.O.): This is the same as a B.F.O. but the term is more commonly associated with single sideband. This is because it is used to reinsert the carrier into the signal to make it intelligible.

Communications Receiver: A term normally used to describe a high quality short wave receiver.

CW: This stands for continuous wave, but it is generally used to mean a morse transmission.

Discone: A form of wide band aerial widely used by scanner enthusiasts.

Feeder: The cable which connects a receiver or transmitter to its aerial. The most common form of feeder is coaxial cable.

F.M.: Frequency modulation. This is a form of modulation of a radio signal where the frequency of the signal is changed in line with the modulating sound. Broadcast stations in the VHF broadcast band between 88 and 108 MHz use F.M.

Frequency Synthesiser: See synthesiser.

H.F.: High frequency. The portion of the frequency spectrum between 3 MHz and 30 MHz.

Ham: A radio amateur.

Jammer: A transmitter designed to stop other transmissions on the same frequency from being heard. Jammers are often used on the broadcast bands by countries which want to stop transmissions from outside their own country from being heard.

L.F.: Low frequency. The portion of the spectrum between 30 kHz and 300 kHz.

Linear: A power amplifier used on the output of a transmitter to boost its output. It is a linear amplifier so that it can be used for AM or SSB without distorting the signal.

Longwire: A term often used to denote a simple wire aerial. A real longwire, as the name suggests, is very long.

M.F.: Medium frequency. It refers to the part of the frequency spectrum between 300 kHz and 3MHz.

N.B.F.M.: Narrow band frequency modulation. This form of F.M. only occupies a small amount of bandwidth. It is used for communication purposes but its quality is not as good as that of the wideband F.M. used for broadcasting.

Packet: This is a form of data communication where the data is sent in packets or bursts. After each packet the receiving station is asked if it received the data correctly. If not the packet is repeated again.

Q Code: A set of three letter codes all beginning with Q which can be used to ask or answer questions quickly and easily.

QRP: A Q code which has come to mean a low power station.

QSL Card: A card used to confirm a radio contact or a reception report.

Rig: A transceiver.

RIT: Receiver Incremental Tuning. This is a control on a transceiver used for tuning the receiver a small way off the transmitter frequency.

RST: This stands for Readability Strength and Tone and it is a form of signal reporting.

RTTY: Radio Teletype. This is a form of data communication where teleprinters communicate over radio.

Scanner: A radio receiver normally for the VHF and UHF bands which automatically scans a number of channels stopping on any that are in use. The use of scanners is becoming more popular as receivers are cheaper and activity on these bands is increasing.

Selectivity: The ability for a receiver to separate signals which are close together.

Sensitivity: The ability for a receiver to pick up weak signals.

Shack: A radio room. It is a term particularly used by radio amateurs and short wave listeners when talking about their stations.

Skip Distance: The distance between the place where a signal is transmitted and where it can be received after having been reflected by the ionosphere.

Sky-wave: A radio signal which has been reflected from the ionosphere.

SINPO: A form of signal report often used by short wave listeners when giving signal reports to broadcast stations.

S Meter: A meter in a receiver which indicates the strength of the incoming signal.

Squelch: The receiver control or circuitry used to cut out the background noise when no signal is present.

Single Sideband: A form of transmission widely used for communications purposes on the H.F. bands. It is generated from an A.M. signal by removing the carrier and one sideband. It has the advantage that it uses less space in the spectrum and is more efficient than A.M.

Speech Processor: A unit for increasing the average power level of an audio signal. It is used in conjunction with a transmitter to make better use of the transmitted signal.

Sun Spot: A dark spot on the surface of the sun. The number of sun spots there are at any one time on the sun will effect the ionosphere and radio propagation conditions.

Superhet: This is short for superheterodyne and it is a form of receiver which changes the frequency of the incoming signal to a fixed intermediate frequency where it is filtered and amplified.

SWL: A short wave listener.

SWR Meter: An instrument which gives an indication of the match of an aerial to its feeder.

Synthesiser: A form of circuit using a phase locked loop used for variable frequency oscillators which do not drift. Synthesisers are widely used in receivers and transmitters.

Transceiver: A unit containing a transmitter and receiver together.

Tropical Band: A broadcast band allocated for use in the tropical regions of the world where the long and medium wave bands are not ideal.

UHF: Ultra High Frequency. It refers to the portion of the spectrum between 300 MHz and 3000 MHz.

U.T.C.: Coordinated Universal Time. It is the same as Greenwich Mean Time (G.M.T.) and is a standard time used as a reference all over the world. The times for programmes on radio stations will usually be given as U.T.C. or G.M.T.

Vertical: This is short for vertical aerial.

VHF: Very High Frequency. It refers to the portion of the spectrum between 30 MHz and 300 MHz.

VLF: Very Low Frequency. The portion of the spectrum between 3 kHz and 30 kHz.

VOX: A voice operated switch used to change a transceiver from receive to transmit.

Wavelength: The length of a radio wave. It is usually expressed in metres.

Whip: A short vertical aerial. A CB or ham car aerial is often called a whip.

Yagi: A form of beam aerial consisting of a number of elements on a central boom. Most television aerials are Yagis.

Appendix II

I.T.U. CALLSIGN PREFIX ALLOCATIONS

A2A – A2Z	Botswana
A3A – A3Z	Tonga
A4A – A4Z	Oman
A5A – A5Z	Bhutan
A6A – A6Z	United Arab Emirates
A7A – A7Z	Qatar
A8A – A8Z	Liberia
A9A – A9Z	Bahrain
AAA – ALZ	USA
AMA – AOZ	Spain
APA – ASZ	Pakistan
ATA – AWZ	India
AXA – AXZ	Australia
AYA – AZZ	Argentina
BAA – BZZ	China
C2A – C2Z	Nauru
C3A – C3Z	Andorra
C4A – C4Z	Cyprus
C5A – C5Z	The Gambia
C6A – C6Z	Bahamas
C7A – C7Z	World Meteorological Organisation
C8A – C9Z	Mozambique
CAA – CEZ	Chile
CFA – CKZ	Canada
CLA – CMZ	Cuba
CNA – CNZ	Morocco
COA – COZ	Cuba
CPA – CPZ	Bolivia
CQA – CUZ	Portugal
CVA – CXZ	Uruguay
CYA – CZZ	Canada
D2A – D3Z	Angola
D4A – D4Z	Cape Verde Islands
D5A – D5Z	Liberia
D6A – D6Z	Comoros Islands

D7A – D9Z	Republic of Korea (South Korea)
DAA – DRZ	Federal Republic of Germany
DSA – DTZ	Republic of Korea (South Korea)
DUA – DZZ	Philippines
EAA – EHZ	Spain
EIA – EJZ	Eire
EKA – EKZ	Commonwealth of Independent States (CIS) – formerly USSR
ELA – ELZ	Liberia
EMA – EOZ	CIS (formerly USSR)
EPA – EQZ	Iran
ERA – ESZ	CIS (formerly USSR)
ETA – ETZ	Ethiopia
EUA – EWZ	Byelorussia
EXA – EZZ	CIS (formerly USSR)
FAA – FZZ	France
GAA – GZZ	UK
H2A – H2Z	Cyprus
H3A – H3Z	Panama
H4A – H4Z	Solomon Islands
H6A – H7Z	Nicaragua
H8A – H9Z	Panama
HAA – HAZ	Hungary
HBA – HBZ	Switzerland
HCA – HDZ	Ecuador
HEA – HEZ	Switzerland
HFA – HFZ	Poland
HGA – HGZ	Hungary
HHA – HHZ	Haiti
HIA – HIZ	Dominican Republic
HJA – HKZ	Colombia
HLA – HLZ	Republic of Korea (South Korea)
HMA – HMZ	Democratic People's Republic of Korea (North Korea)
HNA – HNZ	Iraq
HOA – HPZ	Panama
HQA – HRZ	Honduras
HSA – HSZ	Thailand
HTA – HTZ	Nicaragua
HUA – HUZ	El Salvador

HVA – HVZ	Vatican	
HWA – HYZ	France	
HZA – HZZ	Saudi Arabia	
IAA – IZZ	Italy	
J2A – J2Z	Djibouti Republic	
J3A – J3Z	Grenada	
J4A – J4Z	Greece	
J5A – J5Z	Guinea Bissau	
J6A – J6Z	St Lucia	
J7A – J7Z	Dominica	
J8A – J8Z	St Vincent & Grenadines	
JAA – JSZ	Japan	
JTA – JVZ	Mongolia	
JWA – JXZ	Norway	
JYA – JYZ	Jordan	
JZA – JZZ	Indonesia	
KAA – KZZ	USA	
L2A – L9Z	Argentina	
LAA – LNZ	Norway	
LOA – LWZ	Argentina	
LXA – LXZ	Luxembourg	
LYA – LYZ	CIS (formerly USSR)	
LZA – LZZ	Bulgaria	
MAA – MZZ	UK	
NAA – NZZ	USA	
OAA – OCZ	Peru	
ODA – ODZ	Lebanon	
OEA – OEZ	Austria	
OFA – OJZ	Finland	
OKA – OMZ	Czechoslovakia	
ONA – OTZ	Belgium	
OUA – OZZ	Denmark	
P2A – P2Z	Papua New Guinea	
P3A – P3Z	Cyprus	
P4A – P4Z	Aruba	
P5A – P9Z	Democratic People's Republic of Korea (North Korea)	
PAA – PIZ	Netherlands	
PJA – PJZ	Netherlands Antilles	
PKA – POZ	Indonesia	

PPA – PYZ	Brazil
PZA – PZZ	Suriname
RAA – RZZ	CIS (formerly USSR)
S2A – S3Z	Bangladesh
S6A – S6Z	Singapore
S7A – S7Z	Seychelles
S9A – S9Z	Sao Tome and Principe
SAA – SMZ	Sweden
SNA – SRZ	Poland
SSA – SSM	Egypt
SSN – STZ	Sudan
SUA – SUZ	Egypt
SVA – SZZ	Greece
T2A – T2Z	Tuvalu
T3A – T3Z	Kiribati
T4A – T4Z	Cuba
T5A – T5Z	Somali Republic
T6A – T6Z	Afghanistan
T7A – T7Z	San Marino
TAA – TCZ	Turkey
TDA – TDZ	Guatemala
TEA – TEZ	Costa Rica
TFA – TFZ	Iceland
TGA – TGZ	Guatemala
THA – THZ	France
TIA – TIZ	Costa Rica
TJA – TJZ	Cameroon
TKA – TKZ	France
TLA – TLZ	Central African Republic
TMA – TMZ	France
TNA – TNZ	Congo
TOA – TQZ	France
TRA – TRZ	Gabon
TSA – TSZ	Tunisia
TTA – TTZ	Chad
TUA – TUZ	Ivory Coast
TVA – TXZ	France
TYA – TYZ	Benin
TZA – TZZ	Mali
UAA – UZZ	CIS (formerly USSR)

V2A – V2Z	Antigua	
V3A – V3Z	Belize	
V4A – V4Z	St Christopher & Nevis	
V5A – V5Z	Namibia	
V6A – V6Z	Micronesia	
V7A – V7Z	Marshall Islands	
V8A – V8Z	Brunei	
VAA – VGZ	Canada	
VHA – VNZ	Australia	
VOA – VOZ	Canada	
VPA – VSZ	UK	
VTA – VWZ	India	
VXA – VYZ	Canada	
VZA – VZZ	Australia	
WAA – WZZ	USA	
XAA – XIZ	Mexico	
XJA – XOZ	Canada	
XPA – XPZ	Denmark	
XQA – XRZ	Chile	
XSA – XSZ	China	
XTA – XTZ	Burkino Fasco	
XUA – XUZ	Kampuchea	
XVA – XVZ	Vietnam	
XWA – XWZ	Laos	
XXA – XXZ	Portugal	
XYA – XZZ	Myanmar (Burma)	
Y2A – Y9Z	Federal Republic of Germany	
YAA – YAZ	Afghanistan	
YBA – YHZ	Indonesia	
YIA – YIZ	Iraq	
YJA – YJZ	Vanuatu	
YKA – YKZ	Syria	
YLA – YLZ	CIS (formerly USSR)	
YMA – YMZ	Turkey	
YNA – YNZ	Nicaragua	
YOA – YRZ	Roumania	
YSA – YSZ	El Salvador	
YTA – YUZ	Yugoslavia	
YVA – YYZ	Venezuela	
YZA – YZZ	Yugoslavia	

Z2A	– Z2Z	Zimbabwe
ZAA	– ZAZ	Albania
ZBA	– ZJZ	UK
ZKA	– ZMZ	New Zealand
ZNA	– ZOZ	UK
ZPA	– ZPZ	Paraguay
ZQA	– ZQZ	UK
ZRA	– ZUZ	South Africa
ZVA	– ZZZ	Brazil
2AA	– 2ZZ	UK
3AA	– 3AZ	Monaco
3BA	– 3BZ	Mauritius
3CA	– 3CZ	Equatorial Guinea
3DA	– 3DM	Swaziland
3DN	– 3DZ	Fiji
3EA	– 3FZ	Panama
3GA	– 3GZ	Chile
3HA	– 3UZ	China
3VA	– 3VZ	Tunisia
3WA	– 3WZ	Vietnam
3XA	– 3XZ	Republic of Guinea
3YA	– 3YZ	Norway
3ZA	– 3ZZ	Poland
4AA	– 4CZ	Mexico
4DA	– 4IZ	Philippines
4JA	– 4LZ	CIS (formerly USSR)
4MA	– 4MZ	Venezuela
4NA	– 4OZ	Yugoslavia
4PA	– 4SZ	Sri Lanka
4TA	– 4TZ	Peru
4UA	– 4UZ	United Nations
4VA	– 4VZ	Haiti
4WA	– 4WZ	Yemen Arab Republic
4XA	– 4XZ	Israel
4YA	– 4YZ	International Civilian Aviation Organisation
4ZA	– 4ZZ	Israel
5AA	– 5AZ	Libya
5BA	– 5BZ	Cyprus
5CA	– 5GZ	Morocco
5HA	– 5IZ	Tanzania

5JA — 5KZ	Colombia
5LA — 5MZ	Liberia
5NA — 5OZ	Nigeria
5PA — 5QZ	Denmark
5RA — 5SZ	Madagascar
5TA — 5TZ	Mauritania
5UA — 5UZ	Niger Republic
5VA — 5VZ	Togo
5WA — 5WZ	Western Samoa
5XA — 5XZ	Uganda
5YA — 5ZZ	Kenya
6AA — 6BZ	Egypt
6CA — 6CZ	Syria
6DA — 6JZ	Mexico
6KA — 6NZ	Republic of Korea (South Korea)
6OA — 6OZ	Somali Republic
6PA — 6SZ	Pakistan
6TA — 6UZ	Sudan
6VA — 6WZ	Senegal
6XA — 6XZ	Madagascar
6YA — 6YZ	Jamaica
6ZA — 6ZZ	Liberia
7AA — 7IZ	Indonesia
7JA — 7NZ	Japan
7OA — 7OZ	Yemen Peoples Deomocratic Republic
7PA — 7PZ	Lesotho
7QA — 7QZ	Malawi
7RA — 7RZ	Algeria
7SA — 7SZ	Sweden
7TA — 7YZ	Algeria
7ZA — 7ZZ	Saudi Arabia
8AA — 8IZ	Indonesia
8JA — 8NZ	Japan
8OA — 8OZ	Botswana
8PA — 8PZ	Barbados
8QA — 8QZ	Maldives
8RA — 8RZ	Guyana
8SA — 8SZ	Sweden
8TA — 8YZ	India
8ZA — 8ZZ	Saudi Arabia

9BA — 9DZ	Iran	
9EA — 9FZ	Ethiopia	
9GA — 9GZ	Ghana	
9HA — 9HZ	Malta	
9IA — 9JZ	Zambia	
9KA — 9KZ	Kuwait	
9LA — 9LZ	Sierra Leone	
9MA — 9MZ	Malaysia	
9NA — 9NZ	Nepal	
9OA — 9TZ	Zaire	
9UA — 9UZ	Burundi	
9VA — 9VZ	Singapore	
9WA — 9WZ	Malaysia	
9XA — 9XZ	Rwanda	
9YA — 9ZZ	Trinidad & Tobago	

Appendix III

AMATEUR PREFIX LIST

A2	Botswana
A3	Tonga
A4	Oman
A5	Bhutan
A6	United Arab Emirates
A7	Qatar
A9	Bahrain
AA – AG	USA
AH	See WH
AI – AK	USA
AL	See WL
AP	Pakistan
BV	Taiwan
BY	China
C2	Naura
C3	Andorra
C5	The Gambia
C6	Bahamas
C9	Mozambique
CE	Chile
CM, CO	Cuba
CN	Morocco
CP	Bolivia
CT1, CT4	Portugal
CT3	Madeira
CU	Azores
CX	Uruguay
D2	Angola
D4	Cape Verde Islands
D6	Comoros
DA – DL	Germany
DU	Philippines
EA	Spain
EA6	Balearic Islands
EA8	Canary Islands

EA9	Ceuta & Melilla
EI	Eire
EL	Liberia
EP	Iran
ES	Estonia
ET	Ethiopia
F, FA – FF	France
FG	Guadeloupe
FH	Mayotte
FK8	New Caledonia
FM	Martinique
FO8	French Polynesia
FO0X	Clipperton Island
FP	St Pierre and Miquelon
FR	Reunion Island
FS	French Saint Martin
FW	Wallis and Futuna Islands
FY	French Guiana
G	England
GB	Special Event Stations in UK
GC	Wales (club stations)
GD	Isle of Man
GH	Jersey (club stations)
GI	Northern Ireland
GJ	Jersey
GM	Scotland
GN	Northern Ireland (club stations)
GP	Guernsey (club stations)
GS	Scotland (club stations)
GT	Isle of Man (club stations)
GU	Guernsey
GW	Wales
GX	England (club stations)
H4	Solomon Islands
H5	Bophuthatswana
HA	Hungary
HB	Switzerland
HB0	Liechtenstein
HC	Ecuador
HG	Hungary

HH	Haiti
HI	Dominican Republic
HK	Colombia
HP	Panama
HR	Honduras
HS	Thailand
HV	Vatican City
HZ	Saudi Arabia
I	Italy
IS0	Sardinia
IT9	Sicily
J2	Djibouti Republic
J3	Grenada
J5	Guinea Bissau
J6	St Lucia
J7	Dominica
J8	St Vincent & Grenadines
JA, JE – JS	Japan
JT	Mongolia
JW	Svalbard
JX	Jan Mayen
JY	Jordan
K, KA – KZ	See W
LA	Norway
LU	Argentina
LX	Luxembourg
LY	Lithuania
LZ	Bulgaria
N, NA – NZ	See W
OA	Peru
OD5	Lebanon
OE	Austria
OH	Finland
OH0	Aaland Island
OJ0	Market Reef
OK, OL	Czechoslovakia
ON	Belgium
OX	Greenland
OY	Faroe Islands
OZ	Denmark

P2	Papua New Guinea
P4	Aruba
PA	Netherlands
PJ1, 2, 3, 4, 9	Netherlands Antilles
PJ5, 6, 7, 8	Saint Maarten
PP – PY	Brazil
PZ	Suriname
R, RA – RZ	See U, UA – UZ
S7	Seychelles
SK, SL, SM	Sweden
SP	Poland
ST	Sudan
SU	Egypt
SV	Greece
T7	San Marino
TA	Turkey
TF	Iceland
TG	Guatemala
TI	Costa Rica
TJ	Cameroon
TK	Corsica
TL	Central African Republic
TN	Congo
TR	Gabon
TT	Chad
TU	Ivory Coast
TY	Benin
TZ	Mali
U, UA – UZ	CIS (formerly USSR)
UA1	European Russia
UA10 – P	Franz Josef Land
UA2	Kaliningradsk
UA3, 4, 6	European Russia
UA9, 0	Asiatic Russia
UB	Ukraine
UC	Byelorussia
UD	Azerbaijan
UF	Georgia
UG	Armenia
UH	Turkoman

UI	Uzbek
UJ	Tadzhik
UL	Kazakh
UM	Kirghiz
UO	Moldavia
UT	Ukraine
UV1, 3, 4, 6	European Russia
UV9, 0	Asiatic Russia
UW1, 3, 4, 6	European Russia
UW9, 0	Asiatic Russia
UZ1, 3, 4, 6	European Russia
UZ9, 0	Asiatic Russia
V2	Antigua
V3	Belize
V4	St Kitts & Nevis
V5	Namibia
V8	Brunei
VE, VO	Canada
VK	Australia
VP2	Leeward Islands, Windward Islands
VP5	Turks & Caicos Islands
VP8	Falklands Islands South Georgia, British Bases in Antarctica
VP9	Bermuda
VQ9	Chagos
VR6	Pitcairn Island
VS6	Hong Kong
VU	India
VU8	Nicobar and Andaman Islands
VU8	Laccadive Islands
VY1	Canada — Yukon
VY2	Canada — Prince Edward Island
W, WA – WZ	USA
WH2	Guam
WH6	Hawaiian Islands
WL7	Alaska
WP2	US Virgin Islands
WP4	Puerto Rico
XE	Mexico
XF4	Revilla Gigedo

XT	Burkina Faso
XU	Kampuchea (Cambodia)
XW	Laos
XZ	Myanmar (Burma)
Y	Germany
YA	Afghanistan
YB – YD	Indonesia
YI	Iraq
YK	Syria
YL	Latvia
YN	Nicaragua
YO	Roumania
YS	El Salvador
YT – YU	Yugoslavia
YV	Venezuela
Z2	Zimbabwe
ZB2	Gibraltar
ZC4	Cyprus (British Forces)
ZD7	St Helena
ZD8	Ascension Island
ZD9	Tristan da Cunha
ZF	Cayman Islands
ZL	New Zealand
ZL7	Chatham Island
ZL8	Kermadec Island
ZL9	Auckland & Campbell Islands
ZP	Paraguay
ZS	South Africa
ZS1	Penguin Island
ZS2	Marion Island
2E	England
2I	Northern Ireland
2J	Jersey
2M	Scotland
2U	Guernsey
2W	Wales
3A	Monaco
3B6	Agalega Island
3B7	St Brandon Island
3B8	Mauritius

3B9	Rodriguez Island
3C	Equatorial Guinea
3D6	Swaziland
3V8	Tunisia
3W	Vietnam
3X	Republic of Guinea
3Y	Bouvet Island
4K1	Russian Bases in Antarctica
4K2	Franz Josef Island
4K3	Russian European Arctic Islands
4K4	Russian Asian Arctic Islands
4N	Yugoslavia (Special Event Stations)
4S7	Sri Lanka
4U	United Nations
4W	Yemen
4X, 4Z	Israel
5A	Libya
5B4	Cyprus
5H	Tanzania
5N	Nigeria
5R8	Madagascar
5T5	Mauritania
5U7	Niger
5V7	Togo
5W1	Western Samoa
5X5	Uganda
5Z4	Kenya
6W	Senegal
6Y5	Jamaica
7O	Yemen
7P8	Lesotho
7Q7	Malawi
7X	Algeria
8P6	Barbados
8Q	Maldives
8R	Guyana
9G1	Ghana
9H	Malta
9J	Zambia
9K2	Kuwait

9L	Sierra Leone
9M	Malaysia
9N	Nepal
9Q5	Zaire
9U5	Burundi
9V1	Singapore
9X5	Rwanda
9Y4	Trinidad & Tobago